HELIUM
Child
of
the
Sun

HELIUM
Child
of
the
Sun

by Clifford W. Seibel

THE UNIVERSITY PRESS OF KANSAS
Lawrence/London

Published by arrangement with the United States Department of the Interior,
Bureau of Mines.

Revised and Additional Portions
© Copyright by the University Press of Kansas, 1968
Library of Congress Card Catalog No. 68-17115
Printed in the U.S.A.
Second Printing, 1969

FOREWORD

The year 1968 marks the centennial of man's knowledge of helium, which has been appropriately called the sun element. No other element has had a history so diversified and dramatic as that narrated by Dr. Seibel in this book.

For twenty-seven years after the name helium had been suggested by Sir Norman Lockyer, in 1868, for the type of atom believed to be the source of a newly observed yellow line in the sun's spectrum, the very existence of the element was little more than hypothetical. In 1895 Sir William Ramsay, at the University of London, found that the same element occurred also in the earth's atmosphere—to the extent, however, of only one part in 200,000. Another twenty years were to elapse without the discovery of a source that might conceivably be used for the production of this substance in more than minute quantities.

At this point the scene of the story suddenly shifts from tradition-hallowed centers of learning in England to Kansas, then little beyond the frontier stage, and the intimate and continuing association begins between the history of the sun element and the land of sunshine and sunflowers.

At the turn of the century, Lawrence's Mount Oread was bleak and almost treeless; most of its thoroughfares were still unpaved. Only twenty-seven years had passed since the graduation of the first class from the University of Kansas. The equipment of the recently completed chemistry building was meager by modern standards; however, it included, significantly, an apparatus for the preparation of liquid air. In 1899 the chemistry staff was augmented by the appointment of a recent alumnus named Hamilton P. Cady, a young man in whom were combined a large measure of scientific curiosity, the capacity for precise reasoning, and a high degree of experimental skill.

In the summer of 1903 there arrived for analysis at the University of Kansas a sample of natural gas from a new well at Dexter, Kansas. Although it was soon found that this gas contained an unusually high proportion of nitrogen, it was not until two years later that a complete analysis by Dr. Cady revealed the presence of nearly 2 percent of a component which was not adsorbed by charcoal at liquid air temperature, and which gave the by then well-known spectrum of helium. Investigation of natural gases from other Kansas sources showed helium to be a universal component, although usually in smaller proportions. With the publication of a paper in the Journal of the American Chemical Society in 1907, the scientific world was informed for the first time of a source of helium that was capable of exploitation on a large scale. For ten years, however, the world took no apparent notice.

After his graduation from the University of Kansas in 1913, Clifford Seibel became an instructor in chemistry, and carried out for his master's thesis a study of the so-called rare gases, including helium, in natural gas. When he presented the results of this study at a meeting of the American Chemical Society in Kansas City in 1917, the world appeared to be listening. War in the air had become a reality, and Britain was building large numbers of dirigibles and observation balloons, many of which had been destroyed because of the flammability of the hydrogen with which they were inflated. British military men had become acutely aware of the great advantages that would be offered by the use of non-combustible helium. There were, however, no known sources of helium in the British Empire. The entire American supply, perhaps half a cubic foot, lay on a shelf in Dr. Cady's laboratory, and the cost of production was estimated at about $2500 a cubic foot. At the Kansas City meeting, Dr. Richard Moore of the U.S. Bureau of Mines, a former student of Sir William Ramsay's, forcefully brought before American scientists the urgency of initiating a program of large-scale production of helium.

At this point, then, begins the final stage in the helium story: the development of production to meet the ever-increasing demand for rapidly multiplying applications, from a component of artificial atmospheres to a means of forcing fuel and liquid oxygens into spacecraft engines. Consumption has increased to a billion cubic feet a year, at a cost of 3½ cents per cubic foot.

Dr. Seibel has been very modest in the description of his own role in this development. It seems appropriate, therefore, to close this foreword with the Distinguished Service Citation presented to him on June 1, 1959, by Franklin D. Murphy, then Chancellor of the University of Kansas.

"As one who has demonstrated the magic of applied enlightenment, Clifford W. Seibel, graduate in chemical engineering with the class of 1913, is cited for distinguished service by his University and its Alumni Association. As a student under the guidance of the late Professor H. P. Cady, he took up the study of helium, then an obscure element. Solely through his imaginative efforts, the supply of this substance has grown from a minute laboratory curiosity to a production of a million cubic feet daily for critical use in the government's ballistic missile and atomic energy programs, and also for important medical and industrial applications. He has been given the special title of Assistant Director for Helium of the United States Department of Interior, personally directing hundreds of persons. More than 100,000 others are gainfully employed in connection with the product which he has developed. He is recipient of the Distinguished Service Award and Gold Medal, the highest honor of the Department of Interior, and of the National Civil Service League Career Award. His University proudly extends its accolade to this alumnus for his unique contribution."

ARTHUR W. DAVIDSON
Professor Emeritus of Chemistry
University of Kansas

Lawrence
January 1968

PREFACE

As the only person still living who has been intimately connected with the story of helium since its beginning in the United States, Dr. Clifford W. Seibel, a former assistant director of the Bureau of Mines, now retired, was asked to write the story of helium, and to describe therein the efforts of those persons who, along with him, labored against great odds to produce helium in the early struggling years. They were years of trials and errors, of bright successes, with not a few discouragements and outright failures.

It has been said, "We learn wisdom more often from failures than successes. We often discover what will do by first learning what will not do, and probably he who has never made a mistake, has never made a discovery." This pretty well describes the work undertaken on a completely uncharted road, and the exciting story of success is the accomplishment of many dedicated people who worked untiringly.

The material in this book has been largely culled from a voluminous and fully documented record which is deposited in manuscript form in the Bureau's record files. To gather the needed information, towns in Kansas were visited to check early publications, and trips were made to the locations of the first experimental plants at Petrolia and Fort Worth, Tex. The history of helium in Canada was also checked, as were the records of the early Board of Helium Engineers. Through the cooperation of

viii

the Departments of the Army, Navy, Commerce, and State, as well as the Department of the Interior, invaluable weeks were spent in the National Archives and the Fort Worth Record Center. "Gathering this material," said Dr. Seibel, "was, for me, a thrilling experience, allowing me to relive the chain of events that turned a dream into a reality for which the whole world can be justly proud."

It is hoped that the contents of this publication will provide useful information to the American public. This summary report will also doubtless recall many incidents to those who have contributed to the Bureau's helium program; to friends of the Bureau of Mines who will point with pride to a phenomenal accomplishment; to the group which accepted the challenge of producing helium for dirigibles when the world's supply had an experimental sales value of about $40,000 but would not have lifted a balloon weighing three pounds; to the organization which developed helium from a chemical curiosity to a commodity essential to space exploration, national defense, and many industrial uses, and to the Congress of the United States which supported the program with appropriations and with helpful legislation.

It is hoped that the reader will obtain an appreciative glimpse of the inside story of the thrilling development of this wonder gas.

WALTER R. HIBBARD, JR.
Director, Bureau of Mines

ACKNOWLEDGMENTS

This story would have read like a telephone directory had I named all who have made worthwhile contributions to the history of helium. Regretfully, many whose talents and energies were indispensable to the government's helium program have, in the cause of brevity, been left unmentioned in these pages. I would, however, be neglecting my obligations as an author if I failed to express appreciation to those who must share with me what credit is due this volume.

I am grateful to Henry P. Wheeler, Jr., Assistant Director—Helium, for giving me an opportunity to compile the documented helium file, to prepare the detailed history, and to write this story. Special thanks are due Paul Mullins and his staff, the stenographic force, and many others of the Amarillo headquarters office who did so much to make the undertaking successful.

In order to check and doublecheck all the information, many weeks were spent going through government files in Fort Worth, Tex., Washington, D.C., Pittsburgh, Pa., and Bartlesville, Okla. Newspapers in Winfield and Wichita, Kan., made their old records available, as did the Kansas State Historical Society in Topeka.

x

I am indebted to Dr. Ray Brewster who, as head of the chemistry department of the University of Kansas, made Dr. Cady's notebooks available for study.

With the exception of the photograph of Dr. Cady's laboratory, which was supplied by the University of Kansas, all photographs are used through the courtesy of the Bureau of Mines.

Dozens of persons, many of them old-timers, were interviewed. Without exception, I found them gracious and eager to cooperate and, though space does not permit extending my individual thanks, I sincerely appreciate the assistance of each one.

Finally, I want to express loving gratitude to Thelma, my wife, who worked side-by-side with me in gathering material, encouraged me through each phase of the endeavor, and whose editorial help and suggestions have kept this account from being just another technical report.

CLIFFORD W. SEIBEL

Amarillo, Texas
October 1967

CONTENTS

ILLUSTRATIONS
(Between pages 66 and 67)

CHAPTER 1

THE
GOLDEN
RAY

On Armistice Day, 1918, 750 black steel cylinders, with orange bellybands and tops, attracted little attention on the docks at New Orleans. No one who saw them knew they were filled with a product that had never been seen, smelled, or tasted. Ordinarily, they might have been under heavy guard, for at prices in effect six months earlier, their contents would have been worth at least 300 million dollars. Originally destined for the war front, they were now on their way back to Fort Worth, Tex.

When the United States entered World War I, the entire American supply of the mysterious substance had rested on the top shelf of a chemical laboratory at the University of Kansas. The three small glass flasks in which it was held were seldom noticed. They were no larger than soft-drink bottles and appeared to be empty. They were obviously important, however, for they had been placed upside down with their necks immersed in a trough of mercury to eliminate the possibility of leakage. On their yellowed labels was written in faded ink, "He 1905." Dr. H. P. Cady (see Plate I), head of the chemistry department of the University of Kansas, had filled the containers with material extracted from a gas well which blew in just off the main street of the little town of Dexter,

Kan. Cady often remarked that he did not know why he saved the "stuff"; there was no known use for it.

Then, America was at war, and several million dollars were spent in producing the material under the camouflaged names of "C" gas, "X" gas, and finally "argon." Its true name, "helium," was carefully avoided.

Produced in quantity too late to affect the outcome of the First World War, helium was to play a major role in World War II. Operating in the Atlantic, the Pacific, the Caribbean, and the Mediterranean—an area of three million square miles—helium-filled navy patrol blimps (see Plate II) safely convoyed more than 89,000 ocean-going vessels, transporting troops and war supplies, without the loss of a single ship to enemy submarines. Those blimps were equipped with sensitive listening devices that could be lowered into the water to detect the noise of an operating electric fan in a submarine five miles distant. Subs gave such convoys a wide berth. Admiral Doenitz is said to have admitted that the German U-boats could not really cope with what he called the "Little Zeppelins" of the U.S. Navy.

Now, since the Navy's blimps have been decommissioned, one might well ask, "What is helium's role today?"

In 1930, an answer to the question, "What is helium good for?" would have been simple: for lighter-than-air craft, in deep-sea diving, and to make it easier for persons suffering with asthma to breathe. The only place on earth where it was being produced in quantity was at the government's plant in Amarillo, Tex. Now all is changed. The uses of the gas, already legion, are growing daily. In 1965, there were 11 multimillion-dollar helium plants in this country, five of them owned and operated by the U.S. Government. There was one in Canada. Their combined production is 700 times that of the Bureau's initial plant at Amarillo.

With the advent of the United States intercontinental ballistic missile program, orders for helium rose sharply. During the period 1955-60, the demand tripled. Fortunately, through foresight and teamwork, the Bureau of Mines was able to meet the increasing need, for—denied the use of helium—many of the larger missiles available at the time would have been unable to leave the ground.

Atlas, Titan I, Agena, Centaur, and Saturn rockets all depend on helium in a variety of ways. Stainless steel tubing, liquid oxygen containers, instruments, and even the thin outer skin of the Atlas are welded in a protective atmosphere of helium to shield the weld metal from oxidation and other damaging effects of the air. Helium also promotes penetration of the weld through the material, permits higher weld travel speed, and prevents disintegration of the tungsten electrode. The missile control systems use helium to actuate instruments and valves. Here the systems can be smaller and lighter than would be possible otherwise, because helium will flow faster and respond quicker than any other inert gas. Finally, helium provides the force to push fuel and liquid oxygen to the pumps feeding the rocket engines. In the Atlas, well known as the spacecraft that lifted our first astronauts into space, helium replaces the fuel and oxygen as these liquids are consumed and provides enough pressure inside the paper-thin walls to maintain structural rigidity in flight. Leaks in the Atlas' systems are detected with helium, and the systems are purged with helium before and after test firings. It may also be used as a purge and coolant gas in hydrogen-propelled nuclear-fueled rockets.

Present-day wind tunnels are a far cry from the early marvels which allowed aircraft models to be studied at velocities of 300 miles an hour. Now, with the aid of helium, small replicas of our space vehicles and experimental planes are tested in wind tunnels in which speeds

3

of more than 20,000 miles per hour can be obtained. Helium provides the push needed to reach high air velocities and conducts the generated heat away from the test section. The successful design of rockets, airplanes, missiles, and manned spacecraft is an outgrowth of such studies.

If man is to continue his exploration of space, he needs to know more about the various conditions he will encounter and have to live with. In order for him to be safe, it is necessary to simulate outer space environments with tests which will assure bringing future space travelers back alive. The magnitude and importance of such an undertaking is demonstrated by the completion by the National Aeronautics and Space Administration of two 40-foot space simulators at the Goddard Space Flight Center, Greenbelt, Md. These simulators use extremely cold gaseous helium to produce a near-perfect vacuum like that found in outer space. Larger chambers are planned.

An earlier space environment chamber, constructed at the National Aeronautics and Space Administration's Lewis Research Center at Cleveland, Ohio, uses liquid helium to create a vacuum so low that present-day instruments are unable to measure it accurately, and to provide test areas that are held at temperatures approaching absolute zero (approximately $-459.69°$ F).

The dangers of the Van Allen radiation belt are of great concern to those studying space travel. To offset the hazard, scientists propose to utilize counteracting magnetic fields which can be produced with the aid of liquid helium and superconductors. An electric current, once started, will continue to flow in a superconductor and thus maintain a magnetic field as long as the liquid helium lasts.

The Atomic Energy Commission finds so many

needs for helium, which does not become radioactive, that it is another of the nation's larger users. A good conductor of heat, with relatively low pumping requirements, helium is used in gas-cooled nuclear reactors. The first such reactor in the world to use helium as a coolant was built by the Atomic Energy Commission at Oak Ridge, Tenn. Helium is pumped through the reactor core, where it is heated to 1,050° F at 315 psig, and then is pumped to a steam generator to produce steam. The steam turns a turbine to produce electricity. Helium was selected primarily because of its inertness, especially at elevated temperatures. As materials are developed to withstand higher temperatures in gas-cooled reactors, helium's use becomes even more important.

Small vacuum chambers which simulate space conditions must be leaktight. After the chamber is sealed in plastic, helium is pumped inside the plastic bag, and sensitive instruments check any leak into the inner vacuum tank (see Plate XII).

Many metallurgical processes call for the exclusion of oxygen and even nitrogen, and helium gives a ready answer. About one-eighth of the helium now being produced is used for such purposes. The relatively new construction metal titanium, which is a little heavier than aluminum and a little stronger than steel, was first produced in an atmosphere of helium, as was its sister metal, zirconium.

Single crystals of germanium and silicon, so necessary to the production of transistors, must be grown in the absence of air, and filling the growing compartment with helium does the trick.

There is scarcely a hospital in the United States without a cylinder of helium in its operating rooms. Mixed with combustible anesthetic gases, it not only reduces the hazard of fire and explosion, but it also helps to clear the lungs after surgery.

Household refrigerators are almost trouble-free pieces of equipment that go on compressing and expanding their charge of refrigerant year after year. Part of this reliability stems from the rigorous tests that they receive before leaving the factory. Many are tested with helium to detect leaks in their refrigerant system. Detectable amounts of helium will pass through openings so minute that a quart of air would not leak out in two thousand years. Nearly 15 million cubic feet of helium is used each year for leak detection.

In a new analytical method known as chromatography, which has taken the country by storm since its recent inception, helium is used as a carrier gas. Only a small amount of helium is used in making each chromatograph, but in the aggregate as much helium is used for this purpose each year as was used for all purposes in 1940.

Then there is Telstar. Not only did the rocket which put it in orbit get help from helium, but the signals we receive reach us after being amplified by a MASER (microwave amplification by stimulated emission of radiation), which contains a ruby crystal operating in liquid helium at a temperature near absolute zero. Remove that liquid, and the faint signal from the satellite would be lost in a jumble of noises.

Helium played an important role in developing the gas LASER (light amplification by the stimulated emission of radiation), which is an optical counterpart of the MASER. In 1961, the first gas LASER to produce a continuous beam of light used a mixture of ten parts of helium to one part of neon. Someday, the LASER may be used to transmit thousands of television programs or telephone conversations on a single beam of coherent light.

Helium enables engineers to trace the movements of gas within oil and gas fields. It is injected into selected wells, and its travels through the stratum are checked by analyzing the gas from withdrawal wells some distance away.

The Declaration of Independence, the Constitution, and the Bill of Rights are preserved by being sealed in an atmosphere of helium.

Liquid helium, first liquefied nearly 60 years ago and once as rare and uselss as the gas itself, is just coming into its own. The total production was estimated in 1965 at 1,850 gallons a day. More than 600 research laboratories throughout the world use liquid helium to reach low temperatures that cannot be obtained in any other way.

Electronic computers are certainly among the wonders of modern science. The more elaborate ones need as much as 40,000 watts of electrical energy, and the space of a small house, and require air conditioning. The memory element alone may occupy the space of two executive-type desks. By the use of a closed-circuit liquid helium bath, memory elements no larger than a shoe box may be used with power requirements of less than one watt.

Scientists recognize two forms of the liquid, designated as helium I and helium II. At atmospheric pressure, helium I, the more common form, boils at $-452°$ F. Helium II is obtained by cooling helium I to $-455°$ F. At this temperature, the properties of the liquid helium undergo an amazing transition. It becomes a better conductor of heat than either copper or silver. It will pass through pores that would stop other liquids, and it flows uphill to seemingly defy the law of gravity.

Strangely enough, more helium is used as a lifting gas today in meteorological and research balloons than was ever used in the ill-fated dirigibles. These large balloons reach heights of 20 miles above the earth, permitting observation of space largely free of the influence of the earth's atmosphere. Helium is also used as the lifting gas in advertising and toy balloons.

CHAPTER 2

SCIENCE
FINDS
THE GOLDEN RAY

Considering helium's ever-increasing usefulness and importance, one might well ask, (1) just what is helium? (2) how did it get its name? (3) when and by whom was it discovered? and (4) how is it obtained?

Science made great strides in the nineteenth century, but even by the middle of the period little was known about the makeup of our sun. The spectroscope changed all of that. Every schoolboy knows that, if sunlight entering a room is caused to pass through a glass prism or even a broken piece of glass, a spot of the rainbow colors can be produced on the wall or floor. That piece of glass or prism acts as a simple spectroscope.

Sir Isaac Newton discovered the principle of the spectroscope three hundred years ago, but it took two hundred years to develop it into a practical instrument, one capable of analyzing the light of incandescent vapors to determine the elements of which they are composed.

Astronomers since 1842 had been intrigued by what seemed to be flames issuing from the sun. Visible only at the time of an eclipse, the flames appeared to extend for thousands of miles beyond the surface of the sun (see Plate III). It was hoped that the spectroscope might throw some light on these great "pillars of fire" and pos-

9

sibly identify some terrestrial elements in the solar vapors.

Interested scientists patiently awaited the next total eclipse, which was predicted for August 18, 1868, with the best observation point being Guntoor, India. However, one British amateur astronomer, Norman Lockyer (later Sir Norman Lockyer), became impatient while awaiting an eclipse, and he designed a spectroscope with which he hoped to conduct studies of the solar flames in broad daylight. Except for some unfortunate delays in the manufacture and delivery of a spectroscope to his specifications, Lockyer might have obtained a two-year jump on other solar observers. Lockyer's spectroscope was not ready for use until the late summer of 1868.

Thus it was that Lockyer was using his new instrument to study the sun in broad daylight in London at the same time a French astronomer, Pierre Janssen, was observing the eclipse of the sun at Guntoor, India. The reports of the two experimenters reached the French Academy of Science within minues of each other. Both stated that the chromosphere of the sun consisted of incandescent vapors, that the spectrum was not a continuous one but made of a series of bright lines of various colors. Each knew that such lines were the hallmarks of certain gaseous elements. Lockyer went a step further. He noticed a bright yellow line in his spectroscope which he had never seen before, so he said there was an element in the sun not found on earth. Later he gave it the name "helium" from the Greek word for the sun, helios. However, it was 27 years before that same yellow line was observed in a spectroscope in an analysis of an earthly substance.

It seems strange that near the close of the nineteenth century there was so little known about the air we breathe. In 1890, Lord Rayleigh, a noted scientist of the time, was busy in his London laboratory determining the density of the gases found in the air, among them oxygen and nitrogen. His Lordship knew that air contained approximately 80 percent nitrogen and 20 percent oxygen. He could produce both gases chemically. However, when he compared the weights of equal volumes of nitrogen extracted from the air with nitrogen produced chemically, he found that they were not identical. The nitrogen from the air weighed more. He called upon the scientists of the world to help discover the reason.

William Ramsay, a distinguished professor (later Sir William Ramsay), working in his London laboratory (see Plate III), tackled the problem; and he subsequently discovered that nitrogen from the air contained a new element which he called argon. Ramsay then became interested in determining the physical properties of the new gas and whether it would combine with other substances. His search for new sources of argon led to the discovery of helium on earth in 1895, 27 years after Lockyer had reported helium in the spectrum of the sun.

The technique used by Ramsay was developed by Dr. William F. Hillebrand of the U.S. Geological Survey and was described by him in U.S. Geological Survey Bulletin 78, 1891. Experimenting with uraninite, a uranium material, at his laboratory in Washington, D.C., he obtained an inert gas when the material was heated with an acid. Later, the gas was placed in a tube and excited with an electric current. The light was examined with a spectroscope. The gas undoubtedly contained helium, but because it also contained some nitrogen which Hillebrand failed to remove completely, the helium spectrum was obscured—and Hillebrand missed the discovery of helium on earth by the slimmest of margins.

Ramsay was more fortunate. He learned of the inert gas that Hillebrand had obtained and hoped it might contain argon. He wrote to Hillebrand requesting a sample of uraninite. While waiting for it, he decided to try a local source and purchased about one gram of cleveite (another uranium-containing mineral), for which he paid three shillings and sixpence. Using the Hillebrand technique, he purified the gas evolved and examined it spectroscopically. The spectrum was not that of argon or any other material with which he was familiar, so he gave it the temporary name "crypton." He sent a tube containing the gas to Sir William Crookes, a noted spectroscopist of the time, for further study. Back came the report, "Crypton is helium, come and see it."

Thus it was that the discovery of earthly helium was announced through the French Academy of Science, March 26, 1895, and Ramsay's three shillings sixpence purchase of cleveite sparked the scientific curiosity that was to grow into our government's multimillion-dollar helium industry. However, another 26 years would elapse before any commercial use would be made of it.

Ramsay, a true scientist, was not content to rest on his laurels. He attempted to fit the two new elements, helium and argon, into the pattern of elements known at that time. According to the systematic grouping of the elements, called the periodic table, there should be at least five inert gases; and Ramsay and his coworker, Morris Travers, found the other three a couple of years later—giving them Greek names: neon, the new one; krypton, the hidden one; and xenon, the stranger.

After the discovery of helium on earth, a number of scientists started investigations hoping to bask in the helium limelight. H. Kamerlingh Onnes, a world-renowned scientist of Leiden, Holland, determined many of its properties, and in 1908 was the first to liquefy it. Soon, much was known about the colorless, odorless, and tasteless gas. That it was an inert element and could not be made nor caused to combine with other substances was accepted soon after its discovery. Most gases become cool upon being expanded; helium, however, becomes hot. One thousand cubic feet of helium at normal temperature and pressure weighs 10.54 pounds. Since air under similar conditions weighs 76.36 pounds, 1,000 cubic feet of helium will lift 65.82 pounds in air. Helium conducts heat better than any gas except hydrogen. Helium is less soluble in water than any other gas. Helium will flow through a hole faster and transmit sound at a higher velocity than all other gases except hydrogen. It is the most difficult gas to liquefy. Neon is the only gas that conducts electricity better.

Several scientists started an intensive search for new sources of helium. It was found to exist in the atmosphere as one part in 185,000 parts of air. Ramsay and Travers, together with Rayleigh and other scientists, found various amounts of helium in such minerals as cleveite, fergusonite, samarskite, monazite, pitchblende, and thorianite. Mineral springs throughout the European continent came in for their share of investigation, as did the fumarole gases of Europe. Many of the samples contained small amounts of helium; so small that helium itself remained a chemical curiosity for many years.

The excitement did not spread as far as the United States. At least there is little evidence of an immediate search for sources of the new element. This seems strange, because at the time fumarole gases were being investigated in Europe, natural gas had been known in this country for over a hundred years.

A burning spring on the banks of the Kanawha River, a few miles above the present city of Charleston, W. Va., was described by General George Washington in 1775: "The tract, of which 123 acres is moiety, was taken by General Andrew Lewis and myself for, and on account of, a bituminous spring which it contains, of so inflammable a nature as to burst forth as freely as spirits, and is nearly as difficult to extinguish."

In 1821, a burning spring was discovered near Fredonia, N.Y. It resulted in the first use of natural gas in the United States. The gas seep was accidentally ignited, which caused the local inhabitants to drill a 27-foot well and pipe the gas through "pump logs" to several nearby houses.

In 1825, General Lafayette, who was visiting in this country, arrived at Fredonia by stagecoach and was put up at the old Taylor House, which he found brilliantly illuminated by gas in his honor, probably the first inn to use natural gas for any purpose.

By the turn of the century, natural gas had been discovered in 17 states. Its production was valued at 23.5 million dollars. Nevertheless, natural gas was a drug on the market. Companies and individuals were feverishly drilling for oil in 1903. No one had foreseen the present interstate network of natural gas transmission lines and the city distribution systems that were to make gas available to the general public.

So it was that the people of Dexter, Kan., were filled with excitement when a well was started in search of oil just a short distance north of the end of Main Street. An oil well, they thought, would make Dexter the Pittsburgh of the West. Even if gas were discovered, they would get smelters, brick plants, glass plants, and other important industrial establishments in their little town. Their visions seemed certain of fulfillment when, while drilling at a depth of only 400 feet (according to the weekly Dexter Advocate of May 14, 1903), drillers for the Gas, Oil, and Development Company "opened up a howling gasser." As the well blew in, roustabouts were dressing (heating and sharpening) a bit in a forge only a few feet away, and the crew was torn between the necessity to put out the fire in the forge to avoid igniting the gas and a desire to get the tools out of the hole before they became mudded fast. According to the report, the flow of gas was "enormous." It was estimated as high as 9 million cubic feet per day. Officers of the drilling company lost no time traveling the 15 miles to the larger town of Winfield, where they disposed of many thousands of shares of stock. Preparations were made immediately to drill a second well.

While the drillers were attempting to obtain valves and fittings to cap the flow, the gas was permitted to blow freely through an 8¼-inch pipe for many days. No one seemed to object to the noise, and the roaring well was a real treat to the passengers of the Missouri Pacific Railroad, a scant 50 feet to the north. Conductors obligingly stopped the train in order that those aboard could hear and see the gasser. To add to the din, some of the townspeople rigged a large tin whistle which they could hold in the stream of the rushing gas. This added materially to the noise as well as to the excitement.

Even before the well was capped, however, an ugly rumor started on its rounds. In Dexter, it was said that the rumor was started by a jealous citizen of Winfield. In any event, it began to be whispered that, according to a reliable authority, the natural gas from the Dexter well would not burn.

Such talk could not be tolerated. So, to quell the idle gossip, the citizens of Dexter planned a celebration which would include a demonstration that the rumor was false. As befitting the event, arrangements were made for an all-day picnic and a public barbecue. In the daytime there would be a parade led by a brass band. At dusk, the mayor would mount a platform built for the occasion and explain to the townspeople and guests from miles around how Dexter was destined to become the metropolis of the area. As a climax, the gas from the well would be ignited to form a huge torch, around which the people of Dexter and their friends might dance and celebrate their good fortune.

The picnic and the barbecue went as scheduled. Excitement was high as at last a flaming bale of hay was swung over a pipe from which gas from the well was roaring. To the consternation of everyone (except possibly a few citizens from Winfield) the flames from the bale of hay were extinguished. A second try ended with the same results. The gas could not be made to burn. In fact, the gas actually put out the fire; and when the flames died, the hopes and visions of the townspeople of Dexter died with them.

The story of the Dexter gas that would not burn came to the attention of the Kansas State Geologist, Erasmus Haworth, who obtained a sample for the chemistry department of the University of Kansas. There, Dr. David F. McFarland analyzed the gas and reported that it contained, among other things, "71 percent nitrogen and an inert residue of 12 percent" (though nitrogen itself is quite inert). Since the scientific literature had been full of the discovery of the inert gas helium just eight years before, it is strange that Dr. McFarland did not carry his investigation one step further. Little did he realize that fame was right around the corner. However, in its fickle fashion, it chose to smile instead on a colleague in the chemistry department of the University of Kansas, Dr. H. P. Cady, who, two years later on December 7, 1905, found the Dexter gas to contain 1.84 percent helium—the first time that helium was discovered to be a constituent of natural gas in this country.

It is certain that if Cady and McFarland had realized what an important article of commerce helium produced from natural gas was destined to become, they would have attended the winter meeting of the American Chemical Society in New Orleans, December, 1905-January, 1906, to announce their discovery. Instead, the Society was informed by the head of the chemistry department of the University of Kansas, Dr. E. H. S. Bailey, and the world learned secondhand that helium had been found in the "wind" gas of Dexter.

The scientific interest in helium which followed its discovery in natural gas gave impetus to further research. During the next year, Cady and McFarland collaborated in analyzing some 44 gases, most of them from Kansas wells. The results were published first in the *Transactions of the Kansas Academy of Science* and later in the *Journal of the American Chemical Society* of September, 1907. In discussing the widespread occurrence of helium in the gases of Kansas, Dr. Cady spoke better than he knew when he said, "It assures the fact that helium is no longer a rare element, but a very common element, existing in goodly quantity for the uses that are yet to be found for it." The Cady and McFarland publication of · 1907 remained the sole source of information on the helium content of natural gas until the start of World War I. Without the data it contained, the government's experimental helium project of 1917 would have died on the vine.

Dr. Cady's notebooks of the 1905-7 period are wonderful examples of the "do as I say and not as I do" philosophy. Cady used standard chemical laboratory notebooks, and his Scotch nature caused him to utilize books discarded by students who withdrew during the first weeks of the course. To overcome a few entries, obviously by the first owner, he would start at the back of the book and work forward, and he was not above breaking a few of his own rules for keeping records.

At the start of each semester, Cady would call attention to the printed instructions on the first few pages of the standard notebook. He would emphasize two statements: "the proper keeping of the laboratory notebook is almost of as great importance as the performance of the experiment," and "before the experimental work is begun, enter the date." There were other detailed instructions to be followed, but the only ones Cady did not break in keeping his own books were those requiring the experimenter "to work quietly with no whistling or unnecessary noises." Obviously, he did not subscribe to his own advice, for after establishing that the sample came from the lone Dexter well, his notebooks are entirely silent on the exact date the first sample of gas was obtained. No mention is made of who took the sample, how it was taken, how it was stored. That there was 1.84 percent helium in the sample, and that it was first analyzed on December 7, 1905, there can be no doubt (Fig. 1).

But regardless of how he kept his notebooks, the world is greatly indebted to Dr. Cady for having pointed the way. Today, more than a half century after his discovery, natural gas remains the only economical source of helium.

The origin of helium on earth remains an unresolved question. There is no theory which is universally accepted. Of the two most plausible, the first one says that all, or at least a part, of the helium existed when the earth was formed, and it has been trapped underground ever since. Doubters of this theory ask why the known helium occurrences are not more uniformly dispersed throughout the world.

A more broadly accepted theory asserts that the helium was produced by the disintegration of radioactive elements—a process that is still going on today. Ob-

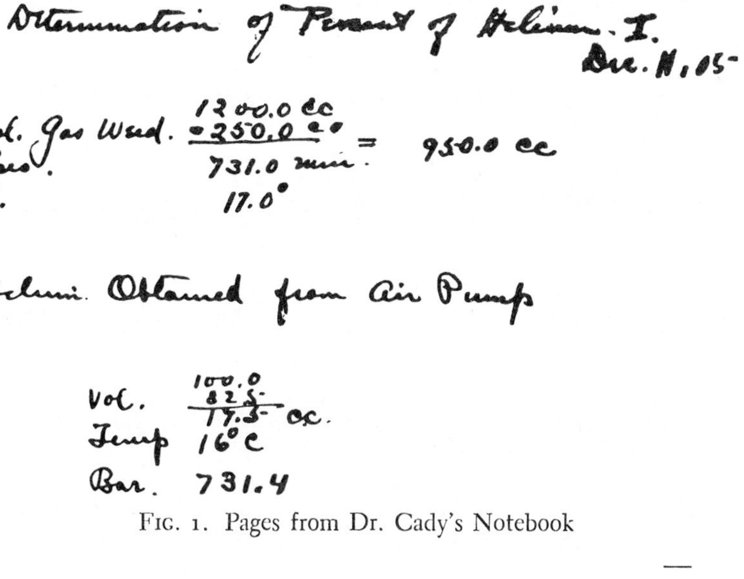

FIG. 1. Pages from Dr. Cady's Notebook

jectors to this theory claim that the known quantities of heilum on earth are far too large to have been produced in this manner. There are other theories and other arguments; but in one respect, there is no debate. Regardless of its origin, a major part of the known resources of earthly helium now exists as a constituent of natural gases; and strangely enough, the analyses of several thousands of samples in the United States show about 90 percent of the helium is concentrated in a small area within 250 miles of Amarillo, Tex.

CHAPTER 3

SCIENCE
HARNESSES
THE GOLDEN RAY

Cady and McFarland seemed to lose interest in helium soon after the publication of their monumental paper on the subject. Perhaps it was due to other activities, or because there seemed to be no use for the rare gas. However, they did devote some time to setting up a new spectroscope. As a means of calibrating it, they made use of an electric arc with iron electrodes. In a hurry to get underway, they overlooked the fact that close and prolonged exposure to such a light would result in an exaggerated case of sunburn. They were queer looking specimens for a few days, with one side of their faces burned a fiery red. I later used the calibration curve of the new instrument in connection with my thesis study on rare gases found in natural gas.

Dr. Cady's notebooks furnished every indication that he and Dr. McFarland intended to investigate the possibility that natural gas might contain other unusual substances besides helium. In those days such a study would have involved lengthy and tedious procedures. The outcome was, of course, in doubt, so they must have postponed the undertaking in favor of greener pastures. As events proved, however, Cady was quite willing to pass the chore to a less sophisticated experimenter.

When I joined the faculty of the University of Kansas as a chemistry instructor, Dr. Cady suggested that I might consider as my thesis subject a resurvey of helium in natural gases. The idea was to obtain samples of gas from the same sources reported ten years earlier, to analyze them and determine if there had been any change in composition. Cady's suggestion was not at all appealing to me at the time, and I accepted the assignment with reluctance. By a queer twist of fate, that thesis was the start of almost 50 years of work in developing helium from a chemical curiosity into one of the country's most valuable assets.

My lack of enthusiasm for the new undertaking must have been contagious, for it soon became evident that samples from the existing old wells would not be forthcoming unless a personal visit could be made to each location. The indifference of the well owners, coupled with a lack of finances, caused a change in the assignment. My new objective involved a determination of the presence and percentage of the five rare gases in natural gas. One large sample of gas had been obtained. Now the unfinished Cady-McFarland project was activated.

As anticipated, the work went slowly. However, by the time of the annual meeting of the American Chemical Society that was held in Kansas City, Mo., April, 1917, my manuscript on "The Rare Gases of Natural Gas" was scheduled for presentation. When I finished reading the paper, still thinking of the many hours spent on a seemingly valueless undertaking, I expressed regret that the study had no practical application and awaited the few questions I hoped would come. Little did I realize that the discussions which were to follow would, like a rolling snowball, soon develop into a full-scale avalanche.

Perhaps it was prophetic that Dr. Richard B. Moore,

a former student of Sir William Ramsay, attended that Kansas City meeting. He was then superintendent of a Bureau of Mines station at Golden, Colo., where he was directing the production of radium bromide. His own thesis, under Ramsay, had been on rare gases. Gaining recognition from the chair, he read a letter dated February 28, 1915, written by Sir William, as follows: "I have been investigating blowers, that is, cold, damp rushes of gas, for helium for our Government. There does not appear to be any in our English blowers, but I am getting samples from Canada and the United States. The idea is to use helium for airships."

"There," said Moore, "is your practical application."

At the time, the idea sounded ridiculous to me. I had in my possession practically all of the helium available in the United States (less than half a cubic foot), and I had sold small amounts of it for experimental uses at the rate of $2,500 per cubic foot. I could hardly wait to engage Dr. Moore in private conversation and to explain how impossible Ramsay's idea was. Even a small blimp would require a hundred thousand cubic feet, and the entire American supply was definitely less than one cubic foot. No method for commercial production was known, and at the current price it would cost more than 200 million dollars to fill a single dirigible. Dr. Moore was not in the least dismayed, and he replied, "You are young! You don't have the vision. It will be perfectly practical to fill airships with helium even if you now sell it for such an astronomical figure." Time was to prove that he had the vision I lacked.

Dr. Moore almost immediately discussed the matter with his colleague Dr. Charles L. Parsons, chief chemist of the Bureau of Mines, who was also present at the meeting. Moore insisted that the possibility of producing helium for dirigibles should be placed before appropriate government officials.

Later in discussing the overall situation with me, Moore explained that for many months he had been wondering what to do with the Ramsay letter. The United States was not in the war at the time, and he hesitated to bring it to the attention of military officials. The United States had entered the war just six days prior to the Kansas City meeting, and the paper on helium gave him the perfect opportunity to present the contents of the Ramsay letter to the leading scientists of our country.

In his letter, Ramsay was voicing the idea of Sir Richard Threlfall, a member of the British Admiralty. Some years later, I had an opportunity to discuss the idea of using helium in lighter-than-air craft with Sir Richard. The Germans, he said, had made a shambles of parts of London by dropping bombs from high-flying dirigibles. The zeppelins often flew at 16,000 feet, an elevation not reached by airplanes of that day. For a time it seemed impossible to counter their devastating attack. Then it was discovered that the hydrogen-filled ships were extremely vulnerable to a skyrocket type of projectile. A falling spark from such a weapon would burn a hole in the hydrogen-filled envelope, ignite the escaping gas, and bring the monster down—a mass of flames. Just when the new antidirigible weapon was reaching its peak efficiency, Threlfall heard with dismay that the Germans were preparing to fill their airships with a nonexplosive lifting medium. The only logical material that he could think of was helium. Notwithstanding the fact that there was probably not a cubic foot of it in the entire British empire, he immediately suggested that serious efforts should be made to produce helium in quantity.

The history of the development of the lighter-than-air ship is a fascinating story that began when ancient Chinese astronomers discovered that certain gases could be confined in a light fabric and rise in the air. In 1783, three Frenchmen (the Mongolfier brothers and the gentleman DeRozier) and our own Benjamin Franklin became interested in utilizing this phenomenon to achieve manned flight. DeRozier is credited with making the first hot-air free balloon ascension in November, 1783. Hydrogen was first used as an inflating gas in the same year. The codiscoverer of the nature of the sun's chromosphere, Pierre Janssen, escaped from Paris in a hydrogen-filled free balloon during the siege of 1872.

During the Civil War, the Union Army used two captive balloons for observation posts. Count Ferdinand von Zeppelin, then 24 years of age, was a military attaché of the German Embassy in the United States at the time; and he is credited with aiding, if not actually fighting, on the Union side. As a result of witnessing the operation of the balloons which were used as observation posts during the war, the Count first conceived the idea of a rigid-type airship.

The first power-driven, lighter-than-air craft was produced by Henri Giffard. Driven by a steam engine, Giffard's airship could reach the daring speed of five miles per hour under favorable conditions. However, it was Count von Zeppelin who developed the lighter-than-air ship into a practical means of transportation. Like most inventors, he had his ups and downs, and he was forced to use his personal funds for many years. Eventually his ideas regarding airship design and operations were proved to be technically sound, and in 1902 he formed the German Airship Transportation Company. Thus it was that Germany had a head start in the use of hydrogen-filled dirigibles as an instrument of war at the beginning of World War I.

A search for a source of helium in England proved fruitless, so in late 1915, when Dr. John C. McLennan, head of the physics department of the University of Toronto, asked the British Admiralty what he and his colleagues could do to help in the war effort, Threlfall immediately suggested that they should investigate possible sources of helium in Canada and the United States. A monetary grant for the purpose was provided.

McLennan set about obtaining samples of gas from Ontario, Alberta, British Columbia, New Brunswick, and even New Zealand. The samples were analyzed at the University of Toronto, and the results were discouraging: compared to the 1.84 percent helium gas known to exist at Dexter, Kan., the gas from the richest source in Canada (the Bow Island field in Alberta) showed a mere 0.36 percent helium.

The Toronto University professor, however, had great powers of persuasion, and through his efforts, the L'Air Liquide Company of Toronto made a "Claude" oxygen column available. Since the unit successfully separated oxygen from the other gases of air, it was expected that it could separate helium from natural gas. Near the end of 1917, the construction of the world's first helium plant, near Hamilton, Ontario, was underway. The available gas supply contained 0.33 percent of helium.

Responsibility for the success of the undertaking was placed in the hands of Professor John Satterly, who was "in charge of all monies," engineer John Patterson, and his assistant, R. J. Lang. During the construction, Patterson and Satterly, wishing to take advantage of any "know how" on the subject, spent most of the month of October visiting with officials of the United States. Their travels took them to Washington, D.C., then to Fort Worth, Tex., and from there to Lawrence, Kan., where they talked with Cady and me.

When the two arrived, John Satterly at once became the center of interest. His hands and arms were bandaged to the elbow, his face was scorched, and a great deal of his hair was missing. He explained that while he was working in the laboratory, a large spherical Dewar flask containing liquid oxygen had broken. The liquid had saturated the cotton batting in which the flask had been packed. Someone had mentioned that the Germans were trying to augment their dwindling supply of smokeless powder by using just such a combination—cotton wool and liquid oxygen. Satterly, thinking they must be joking, remarked "you couldn't make that stuff explode," and touched a match to it. There was a violent explosion. In Satterly's words: "A sudden uprush of fire and burnt wool followed, which hurt me horribly about the face and hands. The hot blast ruckled the skin on the back of my hands, burned my face, and removed the hair from the front of my head. Luckily I heal well." He went on to say that later in his lectures on liquid air he repeated the experiment, taking care to use less liquid oxygen and cotton batting, and to replace the match by a candle wired to the end of a meter stick.

Back in Canada, fortified with information obtained at Cady's laboratory, the two men and their assistants started the plant at Hamilton, Ontario, and in February, 1918, they were able to produce a small quantity of 87 percent helium. Unfortunately, the helium-bearing gas supply at Hamilton became depleted shortly after the plant began operating, and eventually it was relocated at Calgary, Alberta. Due in part to the unsatisfactory gas supply, the undertaking was not too successful, and in April, 1920, the Admiralty "closed its purse string." The plant was shut down and eventually dismantled. Although the plant had been designed in the hopes of producing 30,000 cubic feet of helium per month, the total production throughout its life was probably in the neighborhood of 60,000 cubic feet of a gas that ranged from 60 to 90 percent helium.

Meanwhile, in the United States, Dr. Parsons had returned to Washington from the April, 1917, meeting of the American Chemical Society in Kansas City, and placed the suggestion of using helium in dirigibles and balloons before the director of the Bureau of Mines, Dr. Van H. Manning. The director discussed the over-all situation with the Bureau's gas expert, Dr. George A. Burrell, and requested that he look into the possibilities. Strangely enough, Burrell had given the use of helium-filled dirigibles prior thought. The matter had been brought to his attention by a former student of Sir William Ramsay's, F. A. Lidbury, of Niagara Falls, N.Y.

Burrell wrote at once to Major Charles DeForest Chandler of the newly organized U.S. Air Corps. He asked if that group would be interested in the production of helium for balloons. Burrell's letter eventually reached the attention of Brigadier General George O. Squires. The general was not discouraged by the limited volume of helium available, nor by the selling price. He replied at once, stating in part, "This office will be most pleased to give you every encouragement for further investigation of the production of helium in quantities for military balloon service. . . . " Encouraged by this letter, the scientists of the Bureau of Mines began an intensive investigation. No one doubted that if helium could be produced in quantities on an economical basis, it would be necessary to obtain it from natural gas. However, there were numerous problems facing those undertaking the project.

The chief constituents of most natural gases are methane and nitrogen. The first could be liquefied under normal pressure at $-258°$ F, the other at $-320°$ F. There was not much chance of liquefying the helium, as that would require $-452°$ F. It seemed obvious that the project would require a lowering of the temperature of the natural gas until everything but the helium became liquid. Then the helium could be recovered through a relatively simple liquid-gas separation.

Consequently, a means for producing the necessary low temperatures would be a prime prerequisite for a successful undertaking.

The chief metallurgist of the Bureau of Mines, Dr. F. G. Cottrell, had been investigating the production of low-cost oxygen for use in blast furnaces and other metallurgical processes. His studies had brought him in contact with officials of the Jefferies-Norton Corporation of Worcester, Mass., which claimed to have an improved low-temperature process for producing cheap oxygen. Cottrell was able to convince Burrell that a modification of the Jefferies-Norton process might be successful in recovering helium from natural gas, and that such a possibility should be investigated.

Dr. R. B. Moore, who had started the ball rolling, also realized that the only economical source of helium would be natural gas, and consequently, that low-temperature refrigeration was the process likely to succeed. He knew that the Air Reduction Company and the Linde Air Products Company, both of New York, were producing oxygen by the liquefaction of atmospheric air, and that each company had considerable low-temperature experience. Moore suggested that both of these companies should also be brought into the picture, to which Cottrell readily agreed.

Dr. Burrell was a fortunate choice to direct the formative period of the project. He had outstanding organizational ability, and was an authority on the natural gases of the United States. The fact that he had never analyzed any of them for helium was of small importance. He knew the location of most of the high-nitrogen gases of the country, and Cady had shown that high helium and high nitrogen usually went hand in hand.

In order to crystallize as many factors as possible, Burrell invited a group of the country's scientific elite to meet in Washington, June 4, 1917. Cady was there and, of course, Dr. Moore. One of the most important people at the meeting was Fred Norton, chief engineer for the Jefferies-Norton Corporation. After describing his method for the production of oxygen, he convinced one and all that it could be modified easily for the production of cheap helium.

In discussing an adequate source of helium, Burrell recalled that the gas of the Petrolia field in Texas contained nearly 20 percent nitrogen, and Cady strongly recommended that it should be analyzed for helium. A week later, a large tankful of the Petrolia gas arrived in Lawrence, and I found that it contained 0.84 percent helium.

Further information on the Petrolia field was sought. Fortunately, the area had been studied by the University of Texas and the U.S. Geological Survey, and each had published bulletins. Discovered in 1903, the Petrolia field was initially an oil field. By 1909 it had developed into a gas-producing area of such magnitude that the Lone Star Gas Company had laid a 16-inch pipeline to bring the gas to Fort Worth and Dallas. Other prospective sources of helium-bearing gas were investigated, including the old Dexter field—by then largely depleted, but the Petrolia field remained the most promising.

During the June 4 meeting, Norton had been requested to submit his best estimate on the cost of producing helium. In less than two weeks he advised that his plant would cost approximately $26,500, not including the primary compressors. It would process 2,880,000 cubic feet of natural gas a day, and produce 28,800 cubic feet of a gas containing 94 percent helium. He estimated that the helium would be produced at from $2.10 to $3.80 per thousand cubic feet. The information was received enthusiastically, and shortly thereafter the Navy Department asked the Bureau of Mines to undertake the supervision of the entire project.

Burrell must have considered that Norton's glowing report needed verification, for he sought the opinion of many professional and industrial engineers. They were unanimous in their high regard of Fred Norton's engineering ability and their faith in his process.

The Bureau of Mines relayed the information collected up to July 19, 1917, to the chief signal officer of the Balloon Division of the Army, with the suggestion that $50,000 be allotted for the construction and operation of an experimental helium plant. Later, the joint Army-Navy Airship Board considered the proposal and was so impressed that it recommended helium be substituted for hydrogen in balloons and dirigibles. As a result, the Aircraft Production Board, later to be renamed the Aircraft Board, arranged for an allotment of $100,000, which became available to the Bureau of Mines on August 4, 1917.

At this point it was necessary for Burrell to augment his limited staff, so he borrowed an experienced gas engineer, P. McDonald Biddison, from the Ohio Drilling and Supply Company. Biddison's first assignment as the Bureau's consulting engineer was the selection of a suitable supply of helium-bearing gas. Thus it was that three weeks after the $100,000 became available, Biddison and Norton were in Fort Worth, Tex., discussing with officials of the Lone Star Gas Company a plant site and a tentative supply of gas from the Petrolia field. Mr. Gage, vice-president of the Company, agreed to donate 25 or 30 thousand cubic feet of gas a day. If more than that amount was needed, there would be a charge at currently published prices. Under the circumstances, a formal gas contract was not deemed necessary, nor was one made. The gas company agreed to provide a plot of ground for the location of the plant adjoining their metering station in North Fort Worth, Tex.

While Norton and Biddison were in Fort Worth

arranging for the anticipated Jefferies-Norton installation, Burrell was in Washington contacting the presidents of the Air Reduction Company and the Linde Air Products Company to obtain their participation in helium production. He also arranged, during the latter part of August, for Captain Owens of the Signal Corps to discuss the overall situation with members of the British Admiralty. As a result, Commander C. D. C. Bridge and Lieutenant Commander S. R. Lowcock came to America to canvass the helium situation and to investigate particularly the possibilities of the new Jefferies-Norton process. The arrival of the two officers gave new impetus to the infant undertaking.

At a meeting called by Dr. Manning on October 12, 1917, the situation was discussed by the British Commission, representatives from the Canadian group working on the project, Navy and Army officials, Bureau engineers, and consultants, including Norton, Biddison, Cady, and others. The two Englishmen brought word that the Admiralty was most anxious to obtain 100 million cubic feet of helium at once and wished to contract for a further supply of a million cubic feet per week. They indicated a willingness to pay as much as $1 a cubic foot for the nonflammable lifting gas.

So much enthusiasm was developed for helium-filled dirigibles and balloons that the group recommended the approval of an additional $500,000. No definite decision had been reached at this time concerning a plant design, though several were being considered.

Five days later, the $500,000 allotment was approved. At the same time, the Aircraft Board, established on October 1, 1917, to coordinate the helium work of the Army, Navy, and Bureau of Mines, arranged for a report on both the expenditure of the money and the work to be undertaken by the Bureau of Mines. The Navy representative and chairman of the Aircraft Board was

G. O. Carter, an Annapolis graduate. Formerly with the Linde Air Products Company, Carter was familiar with low-temperature processing. Dr. H. N. Davis of Harvard University represented the Army, and George Orrok of the Bureau of Mines represented the Department of the Interior. Carter made a hurried review on the Norton process. His report, which was very uncomplimentary, carried great weight with the Army and Navy officials. It is not surprising, therefore, that the Navy took action to exclude the Norton scheme from immediate participation in the $500,000 just appropriated. Officials of the Army concurred.

Contracts were signed with the Linde Company on November 16, 1917, and with the Air Reduction Company two weeks later. Both companies agreed to make available to the government a modified standard oxygen plant for helium extraction.

Secretary Daniels of the Navy might have completely eliminated the Norton plan from further consideration had it not been for the British enthusiasm over its claim for cheap helium. Instead, he referred Norton's proposal to the National Research Council, recommending, very logically, that none of the $500,000 be spent on the questioned project pending the outcome of this investigation.

Meanwhile, both the Linde Company and the Air Reduction Company had equipment ready to ship and no place to send it. The answer was obvious—utilize the site selected by Norton at Fort Worth. Under the circumstances, Norton was forced to agree with this arrangement.

The British Helium Commission was greatly disappointed and somewhat embarrassed by the action. They mentioned that they were spending millions of dollars to build lighter-than-air craft, a large percentage of which had been destroyed because of the flammability of the hydrogen. They were confident that if helium could be substituted, warfare in the air would be completely revolutionized. They also argued that because of the strategic importance of this type of aircraft and its heavy cost, great haste should be the watchword. Furthermore, they could not lose sight of the fact that Norton promised helium at less than a cent a cubic foot, whereas they had been prepared to pay a hundred times that amount.

On January 14, 1918, the National Research Council issued its report which said in part, ". . . the committee is unanimously of the opinion that the Norton process . . . is scientifically sound, that it should accomplish the desired result, and that every part of it seems to have been conceived in the light of a clear understanding of the problem and of the means which good engineering would suggest as conducive to economy . . . ." With that clean bill, the Navy Department cooperated fully and within a few days made an allotment of $50,000 to the Bureau of Mines for the further development of the Norton process. This was matched almost at once by an equal appropriation from the Army.

Consequently, Norton was not completely stymied by the refusal of the Navy Department to permit participation in the $500,000 allotment. The earlier sum of $100,000 assigned to the Bureau of Mines was made available to him to enable him to continue work on the design of his proposed experimental plant.

When Dr. Cady returned to Lawrence from the Washington meeting in mid-October of 1917, he was bubbling over with important information, but could not share it with the world. He had been impressed with a need for secrecy, and yet a sum of $500,000 had been provided to produce the rare and, up to that time, seemingly useless material that he had discovered to be present in natural gas. In the wildest flights of his imagination he had never dreamed of such a possibility. He had been requested to see that all notebooks on the subject were kept in code; that was the least of his worries. A person glancing at any one of his several notebooks would have jumped to the conclusion that keeping them in code had been his standard practice. The project was so "hush-hush" that the very word helium was taboo in both correspondence and conversation. The British spoke of it as "C" gas. In America it became "X" gas and finally, to the confusion of everyone, "argon." Only a few of us were privileged to share his confidence.

Perhaps the Kansas University professor was the first to recognize that the success of the low-temperature helium extraction process would depend largely on the solubility of helium in the liquefied portions of the natural gas; that if its solubility was high, the recovery of satisfactory volumes of helium would require more than a simple gas-liquid separation. Little or no information on the subject was available, so Cady decided to supply it. He and I, together with Dr. Paul V. Farragher of the chemistry department, set about determining how much helium would go into solution in the natural gas liquids produced at the temperature of liquid methane and liquid nitrogen. Speed, rather than extreme accuracy, was the watchword, but the solubility data obtained at a pressure of 65 pounds per square inch proved quite accurate. The data showed that fractionation would not be necessary, as the resulting losses due to solubility would be acceptable and in the neighborhood of 10 to 12 percent.

Cady was confident that under the very best of conditions helium would be an expensive commodity. He saw an economic advantage in adding a limited volume of cheaper hydrogen to the helium if an explosive mixture could be avoided. After many experiments performed by Fred Bruckmiller, of the Kansas State water laboratory, and the writer, he assured the Army and Navy that approximately 10 percent hydrogen could be mixed with 90 percent helium, and that a gas of that composition would neither burn nor explode. The mixture was never used, for by the time helium-filled airships became a reality it was cheaper to purify the helium from the balloon than to use a mixture that could not be purified with safety.

The professor also recognized the need to know how rapidly helium would pass through the fabric used for balloons and dirigibles. Knowing that the laws of diffusion did not always hold in such instances, he set about determining what the loss would be. He met opposition from a government laboratory already working on the problem, but a satisfactory compromise was reached. Cady agreed to furnish a small amount of helium and, in return, was given samples of various types of balloon fabric for his tests. By this time, as Cady's principal assistant in the helium work at the University of Kansas, it was my lot not only to carry on the diffusion experiments but also to produce the helium required by the trade. Every cubic centimeter of gas which had been separated during analysis had been carefully saved. Eventually, using that gas and an additional quantity produced by tedious laboratory extraction, we collected three and one-half liters of pure helium. The gas was placed in inverted citrate of magnesia bottles held in an open-sided wooden crate. It was our hope that anyone handling the container would see the delicate nature of the shipment and treat it respectfully.

Dr. Cady, who was blessed with a good sense of humor, said that the shipment reminded him of a litter of pups and that no mother dog ever took greater pains to protect her offspring—a remark which was to take on added meaning a few weeks later. The shipment was placed carefully on board an express car, and I heaved a sigh of relief as it started on its journey to Washington.

Months before, Dr. Cady had agreed to teach chemistry classes in summer school at Stanford University. He had purchased a Ford automobile with the idea of driving his family to the West Coast. He was torn between a desire to stay in Lawrence and continue the helium experimental work, and his urge to put the new car through its paces and see the country to the west. The car, Stanford, and the family won out; the Washington office was advised of the trip and his California address. Those of us left in Lawrence continued working on the various helium problems behind locked doors.

About two weeks after the doctor's departure, a telegram was received from him. The message read, "He is lost; send more pups from the same litter." It is certain that such a telegram would have stumped even an experienced cryptographist. At the University of Kansas it brought utter dismay. We had no trouble deciphering it. "He" is the chemical symbol for helium. Recalling the remark about the litter of pups, it became obvious that the shipment was lost and that another quantity of helium was needed. My entire summer was spent in producing that second shipment. Many months later the missing helium was found safe, if well hidden, underneath some storeroom steps at the Bureau of Standards. What was done with the precious extra supply was never learned.

Meanwhile, with funds assured for the helium project, Burrell, Biddison, and others had turned their attention to locating additional supplies of helium-bearing gas—and well they might, for information supplied by the British Commission indicated that from 4 to 6 million cubic feet of helium per month might be required. The two experimental plants under contract could not possibly produce more than a quarter of a million cubic feet in thirty days. If and when the Jefferies-Norton plant should also get into full operation, the total output would be no more than a million cubic feet per month. C. F. Ward, a gas engineer from Mr. Biddison's organization, was employed to make a quick survey in the hopes of locating additional sources for helium extraction. The only equipment capable of accurate helium analysis was located in my laboratory at the University of Kansas, so all of the samples of gas collected by Mr. Ward were sent to me for analysis. Periodically, he would stop at Lawrence to go over the results of his survey in the hopes of pinpointing the direction of the next trip.

Ward was not familiar with government rules and regulations, and not infrequently he ran afoul of them. He used official government transportation requests for his travel but paid cash for his meals and lodging, which were subject to reimbursement at $4 a day. On one occasion he arrived in Lawrence with but a few cents in his pockets and explained that he had directed the paymaster to send his expense check to the laboratory. Did he have a letter from Washington? Cady had been holding such an envelope for several days and turned it over with the suggestion that if the check were big enough we should celebrate. Ward's gleam of expectation was short-lived. The letter contained no money. The expense account was returned with an explanation which read, "This expense account contains an item of 25 cents for porter tips. You are allowed 15 cents for a night porter and 10 cents for a day porter. Please itemize." That silly letter probably cost the government two weeks of precious time and at least $100. Ward borrowed funds and wrote a transportation request for rail travel home. Two weeks later, back in Lawrence, he picked up where he left off. In the meantime, he had assured the government auditor that a day porter had been tipped 10 cents and a night porter 15 cents, thus arriving at the proper total.

The results of Ward's preliminary investigation

made the Bureau of Mines realize that if production of helium was to be more than just a flash in the pan, a much more comprehensive search was needed. The director of the U.S. Geological Survey was asked to cooperate, and in June, 1918, one of his finest geologists, G. Sherburne Rogers, was assigned to direct the undertaking.

Shortly after Rogers began his helium-bearing gas survey, he was able to obtain the assistance of a number of colleagues to help in the collection of samples. About this time, Dr. Moore requested my release from the University of Kansas for permanent assignment to head the Bureau of Mines laboratory at Fort Worth, Tex. We were fortunate to have the Army transfer to us James B. Ramsey, a former instructor in chemistry at K.U. He was soon making helium analyses at a rapid rate, both samples from the field and those requested by the two experimental plants.

Six months after the start of the gas field survey, three hundred samples from all over the country, collected by Rogers and his colleagues, had been sent to me for analysis. Rogers' report was not published until 1921, but it was to remain the bible on helium resources for many years.

CHAPTER 4

FROM
PLANS
TO PLANTS

With the design of the plants in the capable hands of Linde Air Products, Air Reduction, and Jefferies-Norton, Dr. Manning was able to turn his thoughts to plant construction. Fortunately, he was able to make arrangements with the Quartermaster Corps of the Army to assume responsibility for that undertaking.

The Linde facilities at Fort Worth, Tex., later to become known as Experimental Helium Plant No. 1 (Plate IX), were completed on March 6, 1918, and those of the Air Reduction Company, Experimental Helium Plant No. 2 (Plate IX), on May 5, 1918. By that time, the two operating crews had been assembled, and as the construction workers moved out, these crews moved in and started the wheels turning.

The two helium plants had been surrounded with an 8-foot fence of knot-free lumber. A military guard was assigned from nearby Camp Bowie, and the area took on the appearance of an armed camp—more accurately, two armed camps. The plants even had a "no man's land" between them. Separate bunkhouses had been provided for each company's employees. There was a common mess hall, but it seemed to have an invisible dividing line between the two groups.

When the Linde Air Products Company made its contract with the government, it included a statement to the effect that no one was to be permitted to visit its helium facilities without approval of its superintendent. Approval was seldom given. That attitude was contagious, and the two companies which had been vigorous competitors for the oxygen business continued to compete in their efforts to produce helium.

In retrospect, it seems strange that, while the primary objective of the plants at Fort Worth was to produce helium, neither had provided an accurate means of determining it. Each group had instruments capable of determining the density of a gas mixture, and from that they expected to calculate the helium content. It took an embarrassing situation to demonstrate the error of their thinking.

For some days, Linde's chief chemist from New York had been helping direct plant operations. One morning he brought a container of gas to the Bureau of Mines laboratory to be checked. He said it was their first concentrated helium-nitrogen mixture, and so it proved. It was the highest grade material produced up to that time by either plant. The Linde group was elated. A short time later their density determination indicated a better grade. The chief chemist rushed to the top of the gas holder, opened a valve, and discharged all of the precious helium concentrate. He then started to fill the holder with the supposedly richer mixture. On checking the new sample, I found it to be chiefly methane. It was nearly two weeks before the plant could again produce high-grade helium.

Although the Air Reduction plant, known as Experimental Plant No. 2, started in operation nearly two months after the Linde unit, it produced its first high-grade helium, 47 percent, within a day of comparable production by Linde. However, since the Air Reduction

Company found it necessary to operate the plant on an intermittent basis, its performance remained second-best. At the start, it was difficult to get the modified oxygen plant to come up to expectations while operating on natural gas. A decision was made to check its performance by using air for which it had been designed. Some time later, a liquid was withdrawn. Who tried it first and why, the government never learned, but a messenger was sent for Dr. Moore to come and see "oxygen" or "nitrogen" that would burn.

When Moore, with me at his heels, arrived just outside the main plant door, there was a bucket full of a very cold boiling liquid. Before he could be stopped, a plant operator pitched a lighted match into the bucket and the liquid ignited. Moore grabbed a gunny sack, which had probably been used previously for the same purpose, and smothered the flame. He then proceeded to lecture one and all on what a foolhardy and dangerous experiment we had witnessed. It was obvious that the plant equipment had not been purged adequately of the liquefied hydrocarbons before air was admitted into it, and the burning liquid was liquefied gas, not oxygen or nitrogen. When it was accidentally demonstrated a few weeks later how narrowly we had escaped serious injury or death from such a foolish experiment, there were those who suggested that a heavy concrete dividing wall should be placed on no man's land.

One afternoon just as the shifts were changing, the superintendent of the Air Reduction group arrived at the Bureau of Mines laboratory with a gas sample, requesting a hurry-up analysis. They had made some changes in their process and were in hopes that the sample in question would show that the plant had "gone over the top."

Three tubes full of liquid air were needed to make the analysis. A quick inspection showed that the available supply was inadequate, and since the nitrogen had nearly all boiled away, the residue was mainly liquid oxygen. The nearest supply of liquid air was in Dallas, some 35 miles way. The Air Reduction superintendent suggested making up the requirement by using liquid nitrogen which could be obtained from their plant. Remembering the earlier episode when someone had tossed a match into a bucket of their "inert liquid nitrogen," only to have it burst into flame because of its high methane content, we at first rejected the idea. However, when it was explained that the analysis might determine the ultimate success of the entire Air Reduction venture, the substitution was agreed upon. It fell to James B. Ramsey to make the analysis.

Ramsey was fully aware that the Air Reduction Company liquid might contain methane, that his remaining supply was chiefly liquid oxygen, and that it was highly dangerous to mix them. He carefully kept them separate in the three tubes. However, after completing the analysis, force of habit caused him to pour the contents of the three Dewar tubes into a single beaker. There was not enough liquid to warrant returning it to the storage vessel so he left it to boil away. One of the guards noticed the boiling liquid and asked if he might take it to the guardhouse to show to a new recruit. Ramsey did not hear the question, but the soldier, taking silence for consent, left for the guardhouse with the beaker in hand. By that time, much of the liquid had boiled away and only an ounce or two remained. After placing the vessel on the guardhouse desk, the would-be experimenter struck a match and dropped it into the boiling liquid. The match flared for a second and then the liquid in the beaker detonated. A huge hole was blown in the top of the desk. The beaker was reduced to fragments, some of which were driven like bullets through the windowpanes of the room. One fragment went through both sides of the electric light globe, which hung over the desk, without cracking it. The two men who were in the guardhouse at the time spent the next two weeks in a hospital, and for several weeks thereafter both claimed that pieces of glass which had been blown into their faces worked out and ruined many a safety razor blade. Miraculously, neither guard suffered permanent injury.

The wheels had hardly begun to turn at the Fort Worth experimental helium plants when it looked as if they were about to run out of gas. The government had not thought it necessary to obtain a contract with the Lone Star Gas Company for a gas supply. It was expected that the Fort Worth demand would guarantee an adequate volume of gas at the "city gate" and that the published rates would cover the price.

Now it was announced that the company had a 56 percent leakage distributed along some 42 miles of their 16-inch rubber-gasketed pipeline between Fort Worth and the Petrolia gasfield. In order to stop the loss it would be necessary during the period of light summer load to shut down the transmission line, remove it from the ditch, and regasket the joints. Mr. Carter, the Army-Navy representative, discovered the situation in early May of 1918. Obviously, there had been a misunderstanding. Mr. Lege of the Lone Star Gas Company had a letter from Biddison, the Bureau's consulting engineer, from which he inferred that the experimental helium plants would complete their purpose and be off the line some time in April, 1918. It was now May, and with such a tremendous leakage, it was essential that the line be repaired before the peak winter demand. On the other hand, the two plants at Fort Worth were just beginning to show promise as producers. The helium was badly needed in Europe, and unless operations were continued, the entire investment would be a total loss. To take care of the necessary repairs to the Lone Star 16-inch pipeline, two- or three-mile sections of the line were bypassed. Then, when the old section had been reworked, the bypass piping was moved to another area and the performance was repeated. The cost of such an operation exceeded by far that which would have been required to take the entire 42 miles of leaky line out of service at one time and repair it. The additional cost, $90,000, was paid by the government.

The prospect of a temporary pipeline shutdown was not the only hurdle. The winter gas demands of the cities of Fort Worth and Dallas had been growing, and there was a shortage of gas. To remedy the situation, the Lone Star Gas Company had made contracts which would require taking large quantities of gas through the Petrolia pipeline from the Keyes field of Cotton County, Okla. Since the new supply did not contain helium, it would so dilute the Petrolia product reaching Fort Worth as to make the resulting mixture of little use to the two experimental plants.

In the meantime Rogers, of the U.S. Geological Survey, had been going over the production records of the Petrolia field with a fine-tooth comb. His report on its expected life brought out the fact that in the winter as much as 75 million cubic feet of gas a day was withdrawn. Under such conditions, the field could not remain an assured source of supply. On the other hand, he indicated that if production from the field could be limited to not more than 10 million cubic feet of gas a day, a supply would be assured for a two-year period at least. But the Lone Star Gas Company, short of gas, could not limit the daily withdrawal to 10 million cubic feet unless they could contract for an additional supply elsewhere. It looked as if a double-edged sword were hanging over the fortunes of commercial helium production. A costly solution was finally arranged.

In order to limit withdrawal of gas from the Petrolia field and avoid diluting the gas in the 16-inch pipeline, the company needed new gas resources and transportation facilities. They estimated the cost at 1.5 million dollars. The government had two alternatives: to shut down the two plants, or to supply the needed funds. On recommendation of the Aircraft Board, a contract was signed January 10, 1919, by Secretary of the Navy Josephus Daniels and Fred Lege of the Lone Star Gas Company, which limited the rate of gas withdrawal from the Petrolia field to prolong its useful life and prevented other gas from being commingled with it. Thus, the government was able to get gas from the area until January, 1929.

The difficulties experienced in maintaining an adequate gas supply for the experimental plants forced the realization on Army and Navy officials that, in order to stay in business, gas companies must operate their properties and transmission lines primarily for the benefit of their fuel consumers. On the other hand, the importance of helium to the war effort was not to be questioned. Consequently, in order not to be caught short a second time, the Aircraft Board recommended that the government build a pipeline between Petrolia and Fort Worth. The Navy Department at once started negotiations for the construction of a 10-inch rubber-gasketed pipeline. The right to bury it alongside the gas company's 16-inch line was obtained, and construction went forward rapidly under the local supervision of Naval Lieutenant Ira P. Griffin. The project was finished too late to aid the war effort; however, the line served the government helium activities admirably for a number of years, and then was leased and eventually sold to the Lone Star Gas Company.

The two experimental plants at Fort Worth proved that commercial helium was a distinct possibility. By the close of the war they had produced 150,000 cubic feet, a quantity now produced in less than an hour. The helium had been extracted as a 70 percent product and purified by Linde equipment to approximately 90 percent. Eventually, this gas was used in the world's first helium-filled, lighter-than-air craft, the Navy's dirigible C-7. Since the two plants had served their purpose and proved their ability to produce helium in commercial quantities, the director of the Bureau of Mines ordered them shut down on January 23, 1919.

While the experimental helium plants were still in the planning stage, it was realized that, from the standpoint of the war requirements, their total production would hardly be a drop in the bucket. Consequently, as soon as it had been determined that commercial helium was a possibility, plans were initiated to design and construct plants of much larger capacity. Mr. Carter covered the situation in his report of late June, 1918. Some two weeks later, the Aircraft Board recommended a million-dollar appropriation to build a large production plant or plants at Fort Worth. The Jefferies-Norton operation had not demonstrated its ability. The design used by Linde had proved the most successful. Consequently, serious consideration was given to a Linde plant at least ten times the size of the experimental one and to an Air Reduction plant of about half that capacity.

The proposed Air Reduction plant never left the planning stage, but the company was permitted to continue at its own expense some experimental operations in its plant at Fort Worth. The results of these operations were never made available to the government. The equipment of the Air Reduction plant remained the property of the government and eventually was shipped to Langley Field, Va., where it was stored and later incorporated into the first Bureau of Mines purification plant.

A contract for a plant to be known as Production Plant No. 1 was signed with Linde on October 22, 1918— just twenty days before the Armistice. The company, acting under the terms of its contract, retained much of the equipment initially supplied in connection with its experimental plant. Production Plant No. 1 began producing helium from Petrolia gas at Fort Worth in April, 1921; operating under the jurisdiction of the Navy, it produced 22.4 million cubic feet through June, 1925. Then, under the jurisdiction of the Bureau of Mines, it produced an additional 23.7 million cubic feet of helium through January 10, 1929. Altogether, the plant produced a total volume of 46.1 million cubic feet of helium in its productive life of seven years and nine months.

When Production Plant No. 1 began operating in 1921, the production of helium in quantity from natural gas became a reality. However, the cost was high; in the first four months of operation when the total production was a little over 260,000 cubic feet, the cost of a thousand cubic feet of helium was in excess of $480. Later in the year, the cost dropped to $174 a thouand cubic feet.

It had been conceded from the start that the Jefferies-Norton operation would suffer from many obstacles not common to those of its competitors. The Linde and Air Reduction companies needed to make only minor modifications of their standard air separation units to adapt them to helium production. However, Norton found it necessary first to design and prepare working drawings for practically all of the equipment needed for his plant, and then to have it built and shipped, often by express, from eastern fabricators to Texas. Just where in Texas remained a question for some time. The site he and Biddison had chosen at Fort Worth had been assigned to his competitors. After carefully considering a number of possible locations, it was determined that the best place to put the plant would be adjacent to the Lone Star compressor station in the Petrolia field itself.

Norton and his limited staff started design work shortly after the initial appropriation became available. However, it was six months before funds for equipment

49

were provided. The delay was more apparent than real, for it is doubtful if the various items could have been designed and placed on order at an earlier date. Not the least of Norton's difficulties involved the recruitment of plant operators, a stumbling block which was to remain throughout the life of his undertaking. Whereas the Linde and Air Reduction organizations could call upon expert workmen and technicians from throughout their widespread operations, Norton found it necessary to use green recruits who had little or no experience with the type of equipment they were expected to operate. In addition, there was a national manpower shortage. The living conditions at Petrolia were far from inviting. The situation was not helped when the few who came looking for employment saw a sign on a tent which served as the hospital, "Contagious Area. Do not come closer than 50 feet." A number of cases of measles had broken out in camp.

It is to be regretted that, through no fault of the company, the Jefferies-Norton operations got off to such a delayed start. However, once the overall design was approved by the National Research Council Committee, January 14, 1918, the company was given every opportunity and ample funds to make good its early predictions of cheap helium.

At the last meeting of the Aircraft Board, a few days after the war ended, an appropriation of $36,000 was recommended to continue the experimental operations of the Jefferies-Norton plant. Additional funds were made available from time to time, but Norton claimed that he was afflicted with too much supervision. Certainly, government control with respect to purchasing equipment and hiring personnel did cramp his style. It is also true that his organization was resentful rather than resourceful in coping with such obstacles.

Norton never lost confidence in his design, and he

maintained that if he had been given a free hand to hire and fire and to make modifications of the plant at government expense as he saw fit, he would have made it the most satisfactory method. Nevertheless, two and a half years after Experimental Helium Plants No. 1 and No. 2 were closed, no usable helium had been produced by Norton. The construction and operation of his plant had cost over $1,200,000, more than the combined comparable costs of the other two plants. The project was shut down July 16, 1921, and disposed of, largely as scrap.

However, the reasons for Norton's failure remained in doubt, and the Army and Navy asked the Bureau of Mines to have an independent study made of the basic thermodynamic and other technical aspects of the process. To make the study, the director obtained the services of Dr. Richard Tolman, an internationally known physicist then associated with the Fixed Nitrogen Research Laboratory of the Department of Agriculture, M. H. Roberts, vice-president of the Air Reduction Company, and William L. de Baufre, head of the mechanical engineering department of the University of Nebraska and a former teacher of engineering at the U.S. Naval Academy. These men appointed J. W. Davis, recently a captain in the U.S. Army, to act as secretary, and later this four-man committee became the Board of Helium Engineers. With Roberts as chairman, the group started its investigation on August 20, 1921. The soundness of the plant, its theoretical and mechanical design, and its past performance were to be studied.

The report by the Board of Helium Engineers, dated November 11, 1921, is a classic. Although handicapped because certain fundamental data were missing, the positive conclusion was reached that the Jefferies-Norton system as designed and installed was fundamentally unsound. Dr. Buckingham of the Bureau of Standards was asked to review the report, and he concurred with the findings.

The Board of Helium Engineers' report on the Jefferies-Norton plant was received with mixed feelings. Their step-by-step analysis made it clear that any modification of Norton's plant, in the hopes of making it successful, would be useless. On the other hand, the thoroughness with which the problem had been studied lent weight to their assurance that helium could be produced for $15 to $30 per thousand cubic feet. Since helium was then costing $174 per thousand cubic feet, the Army and Navy officials asked the Bureau of Mines to extend the work of the board to determine how such a cost reduction could be achieved.

The board's first effort in this direction revolved around a small laboratory-type plant set up in the Bureau of Mines Cryogenic Research Laboratory which had been organized the previous year in Washington. The laboratory setup had been designed to take full advantage of newly developed experimental data and a number of theoretical curves calculated by one of their principal engineers, E. S. Burnett. In view of the encouraging report on the little table model's performance, the Army and Navy furnished funds for the design, construction, and operation of what came to be known as the Bureau's Semicommercial Plant. The equipment was estimated to cost $17,000.

The three original members of the Board of Helium Engineers were busy men with full-time occupations in widely separated sections of the country. As a result, John W. Davis, a very capable engineer who first served as secretary to the board, became the leading spirit and active superintendent of the project.

Design work for the Semicommercial Plant was approved by frequent meetings of the board, but it fell to the lot of Davis and his Washington staff, headed by

Chief Draftsman F. A. Large, to prepare working drawings and specifications and obtain bids on items which could not be fabricated in the Cryogenic Research Laboratory shops in Washington. By September, 1923, all of the necessary equipment had been installed in the old Air Reduction Helium Plant building in Fort Worth. F. A. Vestal, former superintendent of Norton's experimental plant, was in charge of construction and operations. Two weeks after startup, the plant was producing helium, and before the month was out, it was in continuous operation at from 25 to 75 percent above designed capacity.

In December of 1923, the Board of Helium Engineers met in Fort Worth with personnel from the Bureau of Mines, the Army, the Air Force, and the Bureau of Aeronautics of the Navy. After seeing the small plant in operation and checking its performance, the group was more than enthusiastic. A few weeks later, when sustained operation gave every indication of helium at $15 to $30 a thousand cubic feet, the Army and Navy Helium Board lost no time in requesting that plans be expedited to cover a plant of ten times the capacity, to be known as Production Plant No. 2. Theodore Roosevelt, Jr., Assistant Secretary of the Navy, saw to it that funds were supplied for the venture. Equal amounts were furnished by the Army. As rapidly as the design work was completed and specifications were written, Bureau of Aeronautics personnel took over and awarded contracts for material and equipment. Eventually some of the details emerged. Two independent cycles were to be employed, one for processing 1.5 million cubic feet of gas per day, the other to supply refrigeration required to sustain the process. It was anticipated that 8,000 cubic feet of 94.5 percent helium would be produced per day.

When a well-known eastern company was awarded contracts for most of the low-temperature equipment, the designers felt that lady luck had them by the hand. The

53

contractor had produced similar and quite satisfactory items for the Bureau's successful Semicommercial Plant. Deliveries were to start in 60 days and be completed by January 8, 1925. The elation was shortlived, however, for it was soon evident that the company would be unable to meet the delivery dates. Anticipating only a short delay, the Semicommercial Plant was shut down the first of February and the crew assigned to assembling the equipment available for the larger unit.

The weeks grew into months, and finally into years. The prime contractor was unable to obtain large non-porous bronze castings which met the strength requirement. It was claimed that some of the equipment as designed was impossible to fabricate. After slightly more than two years of valiant effort, the contractor was forced to concede defeat and gave up. Eventually, the case was taken to the U.S. Court of Claims for adjustment.

The delay in obtaining equipment for Production Plant No. 2 was both serious and unexpected, and plans to build the plant narrowly avoided cancellation.

Officials of the Bureau of Mines and the Navy Department strove in every way to make the cooperative efforts connected with Production Plant No. 2 successful and harmonious. However, it was clearly evident that the preparation of designs, drawings, and specifications by the Bureau of Mines, procurement by the Navy Department, erection by the first, in facilities operated by the second, was as complicated as it sounds. Also, since the Navy Department had charge of the already operating Production Plant No. 1, there were those who felt understandably that the work on Production Plant No. 2 was placed second. After considering the pros and cons for many months, the secretaries of War, Navy, and Interior unanimously approved the transfer of the operating phases of helium production from the Navy Department to the Bureau of Mines.

As can well be imagined, there were many hot arguments on both sides of the controversy. Some in the Navy Department felt that the best solution was to remove the Bureau of Mines from contention by scrapping all plans for Production Plant No. 2. When the suggestion was brought before the Army-Navy Helium Board in late 1924, its members demonstrated they would have none of that by placing the erection and operation of Production Plant No. 2 under the sole control of the Board of Helium Engineers. Nevertheless, fuel was added to the fire when the Linde organization claimed that their plant would soon be able to deliver helium for $30 per thousand cubic feet, and hinted that $15 per thousand was a good possibility.

Had it not been for the imagination and foresight of Dr. Moore, who first suggested the production of helium from natural gas, and Dr. Parsons, who first sought government support for such an undertaking, this story would not have been written. Also, it was the persevering confidence of the Bureau of Mines, based upon a high degree of technical competence, that sustained the interest of the Army and Navy through many periods of doubt and uncertainty in the venture.

The Bureau of Mines did much more, however, than merely provide needed technical liaison, advice, and support to the Army and the Navy and to the private participants in the early experimental efforts. The first really comprehensive helium survey of all of the known gas fields of the United States was made by the Bureau of Mines in its laboratory, located adjacent to the experimental plants at Fort Worth. The analytical work was performed by an augmented crew operating under my jurisdiction, consisting of James B. Ramsey; H. M. Eastman, formerly superintendent of the Bureau of Mines Radium Plant in Colorado; H. S. Kennedy, a former Army flying instructor; Dr. Leo Finklestein; and Walter Cullison, chemist of the state food and drug laboratory at K.U., just home from Army service. The field work was directed by A. N. Dangerfield, an able geologist, assisted by Yancy Mc-Daniels, formerly a lieutenant in charge of the military contingent at the Jefferies-Norton experimental plant. McDaniels had become a national hero a few months before as the first man in the United States to parachute from a plane.

In the earlier Rogers survey, speed was all-important and the samples were analyzed for their helium content only. Now, with sufficient help, all samples were analyzed for oxygen, carbon dioxide, helium, methane, and ethane. The residue was assumed to be nitrogen. It was expected that the added information might shed some light on where to look for helium. At the end of the study, Cady's earlier finding was still valid: High helium is usually associated with high nitrogen; on the other hand, high nitrogen gases may contain little or no helium. The survey was disappointing at the time in that only one important new source of helium-bearing gas was discovered. However, that single find subsequently proved to be worth all the money spent on all the surveys up to that time. The new source was the Cliffside gas field near Amarillo, Texas.

During the initial phase of the sampling program, all reimbursements for expenses incurred by our small crew were made through an Army disbursing officer. After the armistice, this officer was discharged and the receipt of expense checks was greatly delayed. To avoid this, I volunteered to assume the duty of paymaster for the duration of the survey. My good deed nearly became my undoing. As soon as the necessary paperwork and surety bond were completed, at my personal expense, I assumed jurisdiction over three automobiles formerly purchased and operated by the Army paymaster. I also reimbursed the Bureau field men for the expense of operating and maintaining the cars. Several months after the completion of the project, a letter was received from the comptroller general of the United States disallowing a sum of $1,418.99, which represented various payments made to cover maintenance and repair items on the three automobiles. The disallowance was made under a Treasury Department Act which said in part, "No appropriation made in this or any other Act shall be available for the purchase, maintenance, or operation of any motor-propelled or horsedrawn passenger-carrying vehicle for the service of any of the executive departments or other Government establishments . . . unless the same is specifically authorized by law . . . ." It appeared that funds made available by the War Department for use in the helium survey did not specifically so state. The former Army disbursing officer was automatically relieved in the case of similar disbursements because of his uniform-connected service; I, as a civilian, was called upon to make good the suspension out of personal funds. After much argument and letter writing, a special act was put through Congress relieving me of the disallowed items.

Besides providing funds for the field survey, the Army and the Navy each contributed $500 a month, to staff the Bureau of Mines laboratory at Fort Worth. Thus, the six-man laboratory group was held together in anticipation of the need for a team to supervise the chemical work of Helium Production Plant No. 1 under construction by the Navy. During this period, we occupied any spare time on special assignments. It was a dedicated group. Finklestein and Eastman worked with me on studies of the adsorption of helium, nitrogen, and other gases in coconut charcoal. Years later, the information obtained was used in the development of a process by which high-purity helium is produced. Nevertheless, the situation at the helium laboratory bordered on confusion. It was evident that the shutdown of the experimental plants was permanent. When the Navy's new helium production facilities would start operating was undetermined. How long the laboratory force could be maintained under those conditions was a question. It was gratifying for those of us in Fort Worth to learn that Dr. Moore was attempting to form a low-temperature laboratory in Washington, D.C.

CHAPTER 5

FROM
TEST TUBES
TO CARLOADS

Educated guesses, rather than experimental data, were used when the first helium plants were being designed. There was little chance of improving performance or lowering costs until more was known about the behavior of natural gas as it is progressively cooled under various pressures. In addition, there was a dearth of information on the behavior of metals and alloys at temperatures in the neighborhood of $-300°$ F, and it was certain that such temperatures would be required in wide areas of any helium separation plant.

On March 26, 1920, the Army-Navy Helium Board, consisting of Navy Commander S. M. Kraus, Army Major P. E. Van Nostrand, and Dr. R. B. Moore, of the Interior Department, informally recommended spending $10,000 to initiate the undertaking. Later, $70,000 was transferred from the Army to the Bureau of Mines for the purpose, and a Cryogenic Research Laboratory (Plate IV) was soon in business in Washington, D.C. Space for the new unit was made available in the basement and on the first floor of the old Interior Building, now occupied by the General Services Administration.

Getting the work of the laboratory into high gear involved both staffing and ordering of needed equipment.

In many cases the items were not available in America, and acquiring them meant weeks of correspondence. Who ever heard of paying $350 for a meter stick, even an exceedingly accurate one made of special metal which did not expand or contract appreciably with changes of temperature? Despite the price, we finally obtained one which was later borrowed by the Bureau of Standards. Today it is a prized possession of the Amarillo Helium Research Center; there are few like it in the country.

Then there was the gauge to measure pressure with great precision. Dr. F. G. Keyes of Massachusetts Institute of Technology thermodynamics fame had it made on a very special order. Dr. A. G. Loomis, who joined our group from the University of Missouri, where he was an assistant professor of chemistry, and I calibrated it, using a 35-foot mercury column in the great domed room of the Institute. To avoid the complications of temperature changes, the work was done in the wee hours of the morning. Thermometers and various measuring devices obtained for laboratory use required checking, and often the Bureau of Standards was called upon for assistance. The services of a number of instrument makers recruited from the Washington Navy Yard, coupled with the facilities of an unusually well-equipped machine shop, contributed greatly to the success of many of the projects.

Learning that Madame Curie was to visit America, Dr. Moore arranged to have the famous French scientist dedicate the Cryogenic Research Laboratory, which she did on the afternoon of May 21, 1921.

The work of the laboratory was performed by several groups. Dr. A. G. Loomis headed the Physical Chemistry Section and worked on phase composition. Harold Kennedy supervised the Field Survey and Analytical Group, and I was responsible for the design of the helium purification plants of both charcoal and liquefaction types, the solubility of helium in liquid methane and nitrogen, and special studies. Captain John W. Davis, later to become a member of the Board of Helium Engineers, was chief of Production Plant Design.

Harold Kennedy and his assistant Frank Porter, whose initial work with the helium group started at the Petrolia Helium Plant, obtained helium solubility data which remained in use until the more complete information supplied by the Amarillo Helium Research Center became available only a few years ago.

One of the first applications of the laboratory's data involved the so-called railroad charcoal-purification car. Even before the production of helium became a reality, Army engineers foresaw the need for a small mobile unit which could withdraw air-contaminated helium from a dirigible or storage vessel, remove the air, and make the helium again usable. Two special boxcars had been obtained and some compressor equipment had been mounted in them. At the time of the armistice that was as far as the project had gone. Dr. Moore suggested that the laboratory data on the adsorption of gases by refrigerated charcoal gave promise of a method for purifying the helium at an estimated cost of $85 per thousand cubic feet. Since the Forth Worth production was costing over twice that amount, the Army was glad to approve the undertaking. The two railroad cars were sent to the Washington Navy Yard, and the needed equipment was obtained and installed. George Erlandson, whose experience at the Jefferies-Norton experimental plant had led to his assignment in the Washington office of the chief of the Air Corps, was borrowed to take over their operation. Erlandson was able to make the unit come up to predictions, but by that time the Linde plant at Fort Worth gave promise of producing helium from natural gas at less cost, and the charcoal type of purification was abandoned for the time being.

In the interest of speed, among other reasons, some

important phases of the work were farmed out. The Bureau of Standards group developed a method, still in use today, of analyzing electrically a binary gas mixture by taking advantage of the high thermal conductivity of helium, thus providing a check on the purity of the helium being produced. Dr. Keyes at M.I.T. derived equations of state for some of the gases involved in the helium work.

The problem of determining the composition of coexisting phases of helium, methane, and nitrogen was assigned to Dr. Harvey N. Davis and his assistant, Dr. A. K. Dunbar, at Harvard University. Such data were essential to efficient helium plant design. Later, assignments were made to the University of Nebraska, under Professor William L. de Baufre, to investigate heat exchange and insulation materials.

Another "farm out" involved the storage of helium. Dr. Moore was one of the first to recognize that storing a substance of helium's ability to escape might soon become an appreciable problem. It was clear that neither the small oxygen-type cylinders at 2,000-pound pressure nor large atmospheric-type gas holders was the answer.

Dr. Moore had the idea that helium might be stored underground, possibly in old coal mines, and a number were available. The Bureau of Aeronautics of the Navy Department cooperated to the extent of appropriating $5,000 to start the study. A small room in the Bureau's experimental coal mine in Pittsburgh, Pa., was set aside for the undertaking. After being lined with concrete, and then with thin sheets of copper, an attempt was made to fill the chamber with helium under several hundred pounds pressure. For one reason or another, the room could not be made tight. The helium leaked out almost as rapidly as it was fed into the test chamber. After many fruitless efforts, the idea of storing helium in abandoned coal mines was given up as hopeless. However, Dr.

Moore's basic idea of storing helium underground was sound, for forty years later the Cliffside gas field began to be used for the underground storage of helium with marked success.

A wealth of data were obtained as a result of the experimental work carried out by the personnel of the Cryogenic Research Laboratory in Washington. They did much to reduce the cost of producing helium. Unfortunately, none of these contributions could be made public.

There had been a question as to whether appropriate items should be processed through the Patent Office or whether the helium project was of sufficient military importance to keep all data secret. In reply to an inquiry, Theodore Roosevelt, Jr., the Assistant Secretary of the Navy, wrote to the Secretary of the Interior in September, 1923, saying, in part, "It is, therefore, the wish of the Department that important helium activities under your jurisdiction be considered in the nature of a military secret." Thus, many potential inventions which might have brought honor and perhaps wealth to the originators were used without credit and then buried in government files.

More than once the laboratory personnel worked long hours to obtain data, and not infrequently they missed the boat in seeing its practical application. This sometimes happened in dealing with well-known facts. Even before Kamerlingh Onnes liquefied helium in 1908, it was well known that it would pass through the smallest hole much more readily than anything except hydrogen. How this property would affect the ability to compress helium, or the design of valves to contain it, was momentarily overlooked.

The Navy supplied the Cryogenic Research Laboratory with a small compressor such as was used on submarines to deliver air at 3,000 psi for torpedo operations, a high pressure as pressures went in those days. When it was tried out in compressing helium, there was so much leakage by the pistons and valves that the highest pressure it could produce was a weak 800 psi. That attempt had an important bearing on the design of compressors and even valves for future helium plants. As a result of further experiments, new valve designs were worked out which are now being used in the government's most modern plants.

Another early question involved the effect of the very low temperatures on metals and alloys. Fortunately, at least one of the early predictions proved erroneous. It was known that metallic tin would undergo a strange transformation and lose most of its physical strength at $-4°$ F. It was feared that ordinary solder made of tin and lead might behave in a similar fashion. If so, it could not be used in the low-temperature sections of the plant.

With the cooperation of Jerome Straus, chief metallurgist of the Washington Navy Yard, a number of machined samples of various metals and alloys were prepared. The composition of each was carefully determined and its tensile strength tested at $-300°$ F. The lead-tin solder, which was the original cause of the study, actually became stronger at the low temperature and was not adversely affected. Other interesting facts were discovered. The use of steel at low temperature was to be avoided, for while it, too, increased in tensile strength, it also became very brittle and subject to failure from shock. Copper and nickel, on the other hand, became stronger and retained most of their ductility. Obviously, they were to be preferred for low-temperature, high-pressure service. Stainless steel, now a much sought material for low-temperature use, was not available for testing at the time.

Dr. Moore guided the operations of the Cryogenic Research Laboratory with skill and finesse. During the formative period he was able to staff the organization adequately and to see that it was provided with sufficient funds. Moore resigned in 1923 to accept a position in private industry. His place was ably filled by Dr. S. C. Lind, a United States authority on radioactivity who had worked with Moore for many years. Dr. Lind had previously studied under Madame Curie in France. The Cryogenic Research Laboratory was just beginning to hit its stride and would probably have remained in Washington, D.C., had it not been for an explosion of an air compressor at the Bureau of Standards. The accident occurred in equipment not unlike that used by the Bureau of Mines. Fortunately, no one was hurt seriously, although the building was badly damaged.

When Secretary of the Interior Hubert Work learned of the catastrophe, he realized suddenly that he was sitting over a potential powder keg. His office was directly above similar compressors in the Cryogenic Research Laboratory, and although five floors intervened, he was not about to take chances. The order was given to "move that equipment out of the Interior Building." Perhaps the logical place for the new location was at the Bureau of Standards. However, there were those who predicted that such a move would result in the laboratory losing its identity and becoming a part of the larger organization. The Bureau's principal experimental station at Pittsburgh, Pa., offered both a haven and many advantages, so all of the equipment of the laboratory was moved there in 1926. Many of the scientific personnel could not be persuaded to follow, and the work was badly disrupted. However, Dr. C. W. Kanolt, formerly chief of the Low Temperature Laboratory at the Bureau of Standards, transferred to the new location as director of the laboratory.

Less than two years later the laboratory moved again, this time to quarters designed especially for it at the new Amarillo Helium Plant. Dr. Kanolt resigned to enter private business, and William M. Deaton was placed in charge. Deaton, a former employee at the Jefferies-Norton plant, had joined the laboratory staff at Pittsburgh.

The Navy had purchased its first airship in 1915 from a Connecticut factory. Known as the DN-1, it was much too heavy as originally built to maintain flight. After one of its engines was removed, it made a few brief flights; but it could not be considered a successful airship by any stretch of the imagination.

In the fall of 1921, the Goodyear Tire and Rubber Company delivered to the United States Naval Air Station at Hampton Roads, Va., the gas envelope of the airship C-7. The following month more than 1,500 cylinders of helium arrived. This contingent included the helium produced for overseas shipment during the 1918 experimental period.

The envelope of the C-7 had been spread out on the "deck" of the airship hangar. The roof of the hangar leaked, and the weather map showed the likelihood of rain. So, working day and night, the crew managed to inflate the envelope with helium and assemble the "car" underneath it.

At 6:30 A.M., Monday, December 5, 1921, with the wind blowing at 18 miles an hour, the ship left the airfield in charge of Commander Zachary Lansdowne (later to lose his life in the wreck of the airship *Shenandoah* in 1925); Lieutenant Commander R. F. Wood was the altitude pilot; Lieutenant A. T. Sewell, the directional pilot; and G. C. Ferris, master mechanic, the engineman. The ship headed for Washington, D.C., maintaining an altitude of 400 feet throughout the journey. Passing over the Potomac River shortly before reaching the Capital City, it ran into a snowstorm. The weather had cleared, however, by the time the ship reached Mt. Vernon. About 10 A.M. the residents of Washington were treated to the sight of the C-7 (Plate V) circling over the city. Those who witnessed the flight saw the first helium-filled,

PLATE I. Dr. Cady's Laboratory (*Left to Right*) O. Maag, C. W. Seibel, H. P. Cady, P. V. Faragher

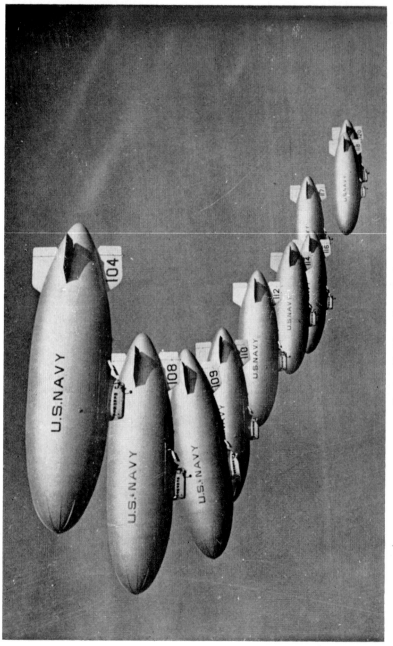

PLATE II. Navy Patrol Blimps

Eclipse of Sun

Sir William Ramsay

PLATE III.

PLATE IV. Cryogenic Research Laboratory (*Left to Right*) Harold Kennedy, J. E. Walters, F. Schroeder, C. W. Seibel

PLATE V. The First Helium-filled Airship

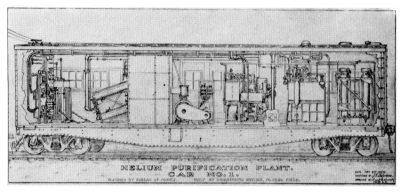

Railroad Purification Car

Helium Tank Car

Plate VI.

Destruction of the *Hindenburg*

Shenandoah at mooring mast, San Diego, Calif.

PLATE VII.

PLATE VIII. Navy Blimp Convoy, World War II

Compressors at Cryogenic Research Laboratory

Helium Extraction and Purification Unit, Amarillo Plant

High-pressure Purification Equipment Experimental Plant #1

Modified Air Separation Column Experimental Plant No. 2

PLATE IX.

Aerial View, Keyes Plant

Aerial View, Exell Plant

Northern Helex Co. Plant, Bushton, Kan.

Crude Helium Extraction Unit, Otis Plant

PLATE X.

Cities Service Helex Inc. Plant, Ulysses, Kan.

National Helium Corp. Plant, Liberal, Kan.

Phillips Petroleum Co. Plant, Hansford County, Tex.

Phillips Petroleum Co. Plant, Dumas, Tex.

PLATE XI.

Leak Detection

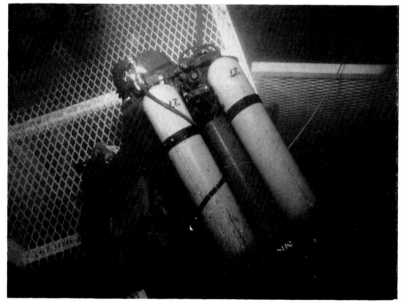

Navy Diver Entering Sealab II

PLATE XII.

Stratospheric Balloon, Explorer II   Atlas at Lift-off

PLATE XIII.

Plate XIV. Surveyor I

PLATE XV. Space Simulation Chamber, Manned Spacecraft Center, Houston, Tex.

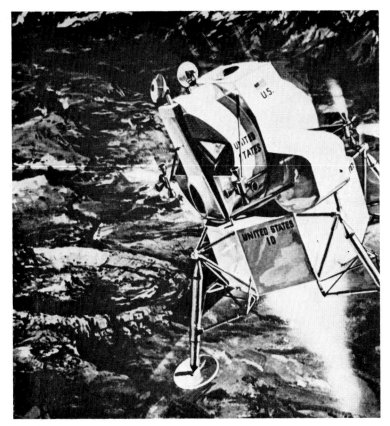

PLATE XVI. Artist's Conception of Moon Landing

lighter-than-air craft flight in the history of the world. The blimp made a brief landing at Anacostia, just outside Washington. There pictures were taken with nearby spectators smoking pipes, cigars, or cigarettes, something strictly taboo during the operation of a hydrogen-filled ship. In the late afternoon the C-7 returned to its home base.

The flight of the C-7 gave helium a big boost, though the gas was costing more than $200 per thousand cubic feet. With hydrogen available at approximately $10 per thousand cubic feet, ironclad reasons were needed to justify the use of the more expensive gas.

The Honorable Lucien Parish of Texas, discussing the subject before the House of Representatives in early 1921, tried to supply the reasons:

> The German zeppelins made repeated trips over England, Russia, and the Eastern Front, frequently destroying railroad centers, munition plants, and terrorizing inhabitants, all of which tended to lower the morale of both the civil and military forces of the country.
>
> More than once in bombing the Russian munition dumps, the German airships let down an officer by cable to the lower edge of the low-hanging clouds, where he directed the dropping of bombs from an airship securely hidden among the clouds above.
>
> Of the 90 or more airships used by the Germans during the war, 22 were shot down, 6 others burned, but the remaining 62 were able to write their record of terror in the hearts of the people of the surrounding territory.

The English, too, were sold on the value of helium-filled aircraft. Colonel E. P. Lucas of the Royal Air Force, who was in charge of all the British dirigibles during the war, is responsible for the statement that the German fleet, upon leaving harbor, was always accompanied by several hydrogen-filled dirigibles and that the blimps provided information concerning the French and British

Naval approaches. Unless they were willing to accept battle, the German ships merely returned to port. The Colonel also insisted that if the British had had a couple of helium-filled dirigibles, they could have destroyed the German lighter-than-air ships and left the German Navy without its eyes, with a good possibility that the British could catch it unprepared and destroy it. The Colonel went on to say, "In this connection, it is not unreasonable to conjecture that with the aid of helium, the war could have been ended much sooner, and thousands of Allied soldiers and American boys who went down as a sacrifice to this great war might have been saved."

The dreadful effects of the zeppelin raids over England had made everyone aware of their wartime advantages. Just prior to the armistice, Congress had considered appropriating funds to build four large airships. Even with the drastic military cutbacks after the war, money was provided to build one large dirigible in this country and to purchase a rigid-type ship from England.

However, the lighter-than-air operations in most countries had been followed by one catastrophe after another. The British NS-11 and, later, the *Dixmude* were struck by lightning. The British R-34 was lost in a gale. The British R-38, which the United States was to purchase, buckled on its trial flight; and the hydrogen-filled U.S. *Roma*, purchased from Italy, hit a high-tension line and burned at Hampton Roads, Va. Such accidents meant a tragic loss of lives, as well as ships.

With this history of lighter-than-air craft, it was not strange that early in December, 1922, Dr. Moore was greatly concerned over the coming hearings which were to consider the future of the airship program. With a worried look, he told me a Congressional Appropriations Committee would consider the question on December 5, and he felt that a demonstration was needed to show the hazards of hydrogen and the advantages of helium. I suggested a simple experiment using two toy balloons, each filled with one of the two gases. He liked the idea. As the Congressional Committee watched, Dr. Moore proceeded with the experiment. Holding a helium-filled yellow balloon at the end of a string, he applied a burning taper. His hand was trembling and the wobbling taper merely seared a spot on the balloon, weakening it enough for the gas to escape with a hissing sound, but without bursting the balloon. When the taper was applied to the red balloon filled with hydrogen, there was a terrific explosion. The windows were rocked, and Congressmen raised out of their seats. Dr. Moore must have been as surprised as any member of the group, but he never batted an eye. "Gentlemen," he said, "if any of your boys are flying in military balloons or airships, do you want their ships filled with helium or will you be satisfied if they use hydrogen?" Afterwards, a member of the group said, "We can't make the Army and Navy use helium, but we can say that none of the money we appropriate can be utilized to fill balloons or airships with hydrogen." From that day on there was never a question about the advisability of using helium in lighter-than-air craft. Later, with a twinkle in his eye, Moore accused me of adding some air to the red balloon to create an explosive mixture—something I never admitted.

A large hangar had been built by the Navy at Lakehurst, N.J., to facilitate airship construction and operation. The mammoth structure, largest of its kind, was completed in 1920. It was 800 feet long, 250 feet wide, and 172 feet high. The hangar was hardly finished when construction started on America's first rigid dirigible, the Shenandoah. This "Daughter of the Stars" was christened on October 10, 1923.

No one objected to the safety factor provided by the use of helium in lighter-than-air craft. Even those who complained of the high price of helium were forced to admit that there was at least one cost factor in its favor.

Everyone recognized that air would diffuse into the gas envelope as surely as the lifting gas would leak out. This caused no small concern in the case of hydrogen-filled aircraft, for hydrogen and air can form a violent explosive. One can be sure that no chances were taken in the matter, and long before such a condition could exist, the contaminated hydrogen was discharged into the air and the cells were filled with fresh gas. Depending on the type of ship and its operation schedule, such replacement, which was both dangerous and expensive, was necessary several times a year. Because of the fire and explosive hazard, the purification of the hydrogen by removal of the air was not thought economically feasible.

Long before the war's end, Army engineers had recognized that the reconditioning of air-contaminated helium could be undertaken with safety. A charcoal-type plant could do the job, but the cost of producing helium from natural gas had been reduced to such an extent that there was no economy in using that method to purify the mixture.

Anticipating the need for a more satisfactory unit, the Bureau had been developing a system that would involve liquefying the air which had diffused into the envelope and removing it from the gaseous helium. The early experimental work on the subject gave promise of great savings. However, it was not until the first of December, 1922, that the Navy asked the Bureau to study this problem as it might be applied to their Lakehurst installation. The plant suggested was of the liquefaction type, and it was to be installed in a building near the big hangar. The estimated cost was $135,000.

The work was started March 13, 1923. I was in charge of the project for the Bureau of Mines, with C. F. Cook, a brilliant engineer, in charge of construction. It soon became evident that unanticipated facilities would be required. The *Shenandoah* had 22 separate gas cells, and each would need means for the withdrawal of air-contaminated gas and a supply of purified helium. To permit the necessary operations, appropriate transmission pipelines were added to the Bureau of Mines assignment. Another extra involved the installation of a 6-inch welded pipeline with 22 outlets in the roof of the hangar. It ran the full length of the building. Since the *Shenandoah* was under construction directly underneath, the lack of accidents during construction of the pipeline bordered on the miraculous.

The Lakehurst Purification Plant was put through a series of trial runs starting in April, and by the first of July, 1923, it was officially turned over to the Navy Department. Later, the commanding officer at Lakehurst wrote the Department of the Interior, "The plant has been operated with complete satisfaction to everyone concerned." And well he might be pleased. Whereas helium produced at Fort Worth, Tex., for the fiscal year just passed had cost $120.22 per thousand cubic feet, the cost of producing an equal volume by purification in the new plant was scarcely $2. The plant had cost $7,000 less than predicted.

During the construction of the purification plant, an event took place which surely demonstrated in a dramatic fashion the value of using a nonflammable gas as the lifting medium for dirigibles.

Getting the *Shenandoah* in and out of the hangar was a ticklish operation at best, and if there was a cross-hangar wind of any magnitude, it was too dangerous to be attempted. If the ship was caught out on maneuvers in such a wind, the 171-foot mooring mast and its little elevator were expected to provide a port in the storm. Though the ship had never been on the mast in a wind much over 35 miles an hour, every calculation attested that all factors involved were good for a gale of 50 miles an hour. Such a blow was eagerly awaited. Each morning at the officers' mess, the aerologist was queried as to the prospects. Finally the day arrived when he announced at breakfast, "It may be calm now, but you will get your 50-mile wind before tonight." The *Shenandoah* was "walked" from the hangar by a 200-man ground force and moored to the mast. By noon the wind had increased to nearly 30 miles an hour, still far below the desired figure. The group learned at lunch that the worried look on the face of the aerologist was justified. He was predicting a 70-mile "whole gale." That was neither bargained for nor wanted, and the wind was already so high that the ship could not be returned to the hangar. All were sure the "Daughter of the Stars" would be safer running with the wind, and preparations were being made to cut her loose from the mast. Before that could be accomplished, the wind took matters into its own hands. Gusts developed that registered 70 miles per hour. Something had to give. Suddenly the good ship *Shenandoah* was torn from the mast, leaving behind part of her forward structure and rupturing the first two helium cells. She started to settle by the nose. But for the well-trained personnel, she would have become a pile of wreckage at the base of the mooring mast. However, with the first sign of the loss of buoyancy in the forward section, nearly two tons of ballast was jettisoned from the nose of the ship and she slowly but majestically rose to meet the gale. Once traveling with the wind, all was well, and hours later the ship returned safely to Lakehurst. The crew became national heroes, little the worse for their experience. All who witnessed the near-catastrophe were certain that if the ship had contained flammable hydrogen instead of the inert helium, it would have become a funeral pyre, as did the *Hindenburg* (Plate VII) a few years later.

In October, 1924, the *Shenandoah* (Plate VII) crossed the United States on a 9,000 mile round-trip from

Lakehurst, N.J. Stops were made at Fort Worth, Tex., San Diego, Calif., and Tacoma, Wash. The return flight was by essentially the same route. Total elapsed time for the trip was 680 hours and 56 minutes. According to the log, the airship spent 235 hours and one minute in flight; 258 hours and 33 minutes in the air; and 187 hours and 22 minutes moored. Atmospheric conditions often required the ship to remain in the air for several hours after arrival. The effect of altitude and the heat of the sun expanded the helium gas so that on approaching the mooring mast time was required for the helium to contract and cool before the ship could be brought down for mooring. It was possible to dock the ship sooner, but to do so would have required venting and wasting helium.

Almost a year later, on September 3, 1925, the *Shenandoah* failed structurally in a thunderstorm near Ava, Ohio, and crashed, killing 14 members of the 43-man crew.

During the two-year period starting with the spring of 1925, a number of events took place which greatly influenced the future of helium. The first and most far-reaching was the passage of the first Helium Conservation Act on March 3, 1925. It placed the responsibility for all government helium production in the Bureau of Mines. It also authorized or provided for the purchase, lease, or condemnation of land, conservation of helium gas, construction and operation of helium plants, conducting experimental work, and the leasing of helium under certain conditions.

Then, a number of dramatic new uses for helium appeared on the horizon. Early in 1925, Dr. R. R. Sayers of the Public Health Service, working on behalf of the Bureau of Mines, together with the Bureau's W. P. Yant and J. H. Hildebrand, published their startling research involving the use of an artificial breathing mixture of helium and oxygen. In turn, this led to the use of helium in deep sea diving and in the treatment of asthma.

Deep sea divers complained, often and bitterly, not so much about the hardships or dangers of working on the ocean floor, but of the length of time it took to bring the worker to the surface. However, they knew that to hurry their ascent only increased their chances of getting the dreaded bends. Every minute a diver worked "down under" more and more nitrogen from the compressed air he breathed dissolved in his blood. If he was brought to the surface too rapidly, the nitrogen in the bloodstream was liberated as bubbles and caused the painful bends, which could prove fatal. By substituting the much less soluble helium for nitrogen, the diver could work at greater depths for longer periods and return to the surface in a fraction of the time normally required. More important, his chance of getting the bends was greatly reduced.

Dr. S. C. Lind, who was destined to be the last chief chemist of the Bureau, had resigned in 1925. This event, coupled with the requirements of the new Helium Act, made necessary a reorganization of the entire Bureau of Mines helium program. R. A. Cattell, superintendent of the Bureau of Mines Bartlesville Station, was transferred to Washington and placed in overall charge.

"Shorty" Cattell brought to the enlarged undertaking unusual ability and a dedication unmatched in government service. Hours meant nothing to the chief of the new Helium Division, which was lucky, as he found himself surrounded by problems. He inherited one of the most pressing from the Navy: what to do about the helium gas supply for the Fort Worth plant.

Back in 1917, the Petrolia field had unquestionably been the best source of helium in the country. By 1924, however, declining production, though predicted, had become a grave concern. Just when the *Los Angeles* and the *Shenandoah* were demanding ever-increasing amounts of helium, a critical helium-bearing gas shortage had developed. For many months prior to the transfer of all helium operations to the Bureau of Mines, Navy officials had been considering the possibilities of utilizing the gas of the Nocona, Tex., field, located some 20 miles from their Fort Worth pipeline. The gas contained as much helium as the Petrolia gas. The Navy plans had progressed to the point where a pipeline right-of-way had been surveyed between the Nocona field and the Petrolia field pipeline. The Navy was very anxious to have the Bureau continue this project.

Cattell was well aware of the immediate and pressing need for helium-bearing gas, but he also realized that the lasting success of the entire program was dependent on an adequate long-range supply. He had reason to believe the Nocona field would not solve the problem. The survey prepared by his former Bartlesville gas engineer, Ken Slater, left little room for argument. Oil production from the field was valued at $40,000 per day, that of the gas at only $300. Wells were allowed to "blow open" for months, hoping they would develop into oil producers. Nocona gas did not burn well, and marketing the residue from the helium plant would be difficult. Besides, "Shorty" knew of a better proposition.

In the spring of 1920, after many trials and tribulations, including running out of money and having a driller run out on his contract, the Tuck Trigg well was brought in by a private company in what was to become the Cliffside field. The nearest town, Amarillo, Tex., was adequately supplied with gas from another source, and there was no market for the gas from the new source. However, a sample of the gas had been collected shortly after the well was completed, and the Bureau of Mines' Fort Worth laboratory had reported more than 1.5 percent helium. In their general report on the overall helium situation of May 27, 1921, Captain Davis, Dr. Andrew Stewart, who joined the Bureau of Mines in June, 1918, and later became assistant chief of the Helium Division, and J. O. Lewis, then superintendent of the Bartlesville Station, pointed out its potential. They recommended purchasing the Cliffside field and even predicted the possible purchase price with unbelievable accuracy. To bring the report up to date, Mr. Cattell had the area resurveyed; the results were reassuring.

The 50,000-acre Cliffside field had many advantages. The gas pressure was a little over 700 psi, much higher than at Nocona. The gas had nearly twice the helium content of Nocona gas. It was a virgin field. There was sufficient gas to provide 100 years of helium production at the going rate of demand. The lease and royalty rights were controlled by not over six companies or individuals. Best of all, the preliminary investigations had indicated that the government might purchase the entire field at an attractive price. The sale of plant residue gas seemed assured. Cattell was so convinced that the best course was to build a plant to tap the Cliffside field gas that he decided to do so even in the face of stiff opposition from the Navy. Of his many wise and profitable decisions, the ones to move the helium production activity to Amarillo and to acquire the gas rights to the Cliffside field are among the most outstanding and rewarding.

Aided by his Washington assistant, Harold Kennedy, Cattell began negotiating for the desired rights. Most of the 50,000-acre field had been leased in two large blocks. The first "operating agreement" was signed May 17, 1927. Some of the transactions were not easy. Most of the desired royalty rights were controlled by three individuals, who together owned over a million acres in the Texas Panhandle. None was anxious to part with any of his land or gas rights. However, after reaching an agreement, one of the three offered to give the government a plant site. When the prospective donor, W. H. Bush, learned that an ample supply of water was as important as the plant site, he had a ready answer. He would have a well drilled; he was certain it would develop the water. Then he would sell the needed land for the cost of the well. Thus it was that the 18½-acre plant site on the outskirts of Amarillo, Tex., with a 300-gallon-per-minute water well, cost the government exactly $746.76.

Meanwhile the outstanding success of the Lakehurst purification plant, built by the Bureau of Mines for the Navy, was most gratifying. This practically guaranteed a request from the Army for a mobile helium purification plant, the need for which had been recognized even before the war's close. Anticipating such a request, I had a group working on a unit that could replace an older charcoal purification unit mounted in a railroad car. The new unit was designed to use the compressors originally supplied with the car so that its purification capacity was limited to about 1,000 cubic feet of helium per hour.

The plans were hardly finished when the inquiry came. Back went the reply. A small experimental lique-faction-type plant had been set up in the Cryogenic Research Laboratory (Plate IX) and given a thorough tryout. The results were so encouraging that the Bureau of Mines had no hesitation in recommending it. Furthermore, the plant would be designed to purify as much helium as the charcoal unit and to produce 97 or 98 percent helium. The best news was saved for last. The Bureau of Mines outlined a cooperative plan whereby one of the old charcoal purification cars (Plate VI) could be converted to the new type for $25,000. Even more startling, the actual purification of helium could be accomplished for a fraction of the cost of purifying by charcoal. The estimate was based on the assumption that the assembly would be made by employees of the Army at an airfield with machine shop facilities. As may be imagined, the offer was promptly accepted. One of the old charcoal purification cars was shipped to McCook Field, Dayton, Ohio, where construction was begun in November, 1925.

The Army crew assigned to the undertaking was under the supervision of J. F. Bolgiano, a former officer from the Omaha, Neb., Balloon School. Bolgiano had small knowledge of the work he was called upon to supervise but rated A-1 for effort. His crew was a willing and likeable lot who made brawn and enthusiasm substitute for know-how.

Reports reaching me from McCook indicated that work was going well. However, when I arrived in Dayton to witness a pressure test of the assembled equipment, I felt as though the rug had been jerked from under me. It sounded as if every pipe joint in the car leaked. They were so bad that there was no alternative to tearing out all of the high-pressure helium piping and starting over.

Realizing the difficulty stemmed from the inexperience of the crew, I established a pipefitting school. After a two-week course, which included passing a practical test, a fresh start was made. At this juncture, I decided to assume active charge at Dayton. L. R. Cartier, a member of the Scott Field hydrogen plant crew who would later have charge of operating the car, was detailed to the project, and he rendered yeoman service as my chief assistant. Each man was now assigned to a specific area, with the understanding that when the final pressure test was made, he would stand alongside his own work to insure that no innocent man would be injured in case of an explosion. This time there were no leaks.

The purification car was completed the last of May, 1926, and was shipped to Scott Field, Belleville, Ill., the home of the Army's lighter-than-air operations. There it was placed in the hands of civilian personnel headed by Cartier and supervised by Sergeant J. H. Bertram of the Army. After a series of successful tests, the car was officially turned over to the Air Corps the first of July, 1926. Its performance exceeded the predictions of the Bureau of Mines, and the financial accounting showed a balance of nearly $1,000.

Although the small liquefaction-type railroad unit continued to give an excellent account of itself, the requirements, due to increased flying at Scott Field, were more than it could handle. Early in 1927, Colonel Chandler of the Air Corps asked the Bureau for a solution. By this time the operating crew of the purification unit had demonstrated both its ability and versatility, and another cooperative venture was recommended. A desirable unused building was available. The plant would be erected by the Scott Field "gas plant boys." I was to provide the design and construction drawings and what supervision was necessary. Some of the more expensive parts were available from spare equipment at various Army installations, such as the Muscle Shoals Nitrate Plant. The Bureau of Mines would supply all missing links at an estimated cost of $30,000. The result would be a plant to process 10,000 cubic feet of crude helium per hour, ten times the capacity of the railroad car. From the start, the crew was determined to make the new plant a showplace. I was proud of this black and silver beauty and of the fact that its performance lived up to its looks.

"Shorty" Cattell, who successfully directed the helium work through many troubled times, inherited another problem which became increasingly acute: what to do about the failure to obtain the needed equipment which had been ordered for more than one and a half years for Fort Worth Production Plant No. 2. By the latter part of 1926, it was evident that, in spite of repeated efforts, the company would be unable to deliver acceptable equipment. In desperation, Cattell ordered that substitute items be provided, if possible, and if that failed, the entire plant was to be redesigned.

By this time the market for purification plants had become saturated, and I was pressed into service to help get Production Plant No. 2 out of the doldrums. George Erlandson, who had worked so effectively on the charcoal cars, had been transferred from the Washington office of the Air Corps to the Bureau of Mines at Fort Worth as Cook's assistant. After a few false starts, the three of us agreed to apply experience gained in building and operating purification plants, and Production Plant No. 2 was redesigned. Some nine months later the new plant was consistently processing 2.5 million cubic feet of gas a day and was recovering 96 percent of the contained helium. Though put together with makeshift equipment, the plant demonstrated that it could cut the going price of helium in half.

Even before funds for the extended helium program became available, Mr. Cattell had decided that Cook and I would have joint responsibility for the design and construction of the new plant at Amarillo, Tex. Aided by George Erlandson, E. S. Burnett, and others, we set up shop at the Fort Worth plant and gave the new endeavor our full attention. In order to release Cook for the new assignment, his assistant, E. P. Hayes, assumed liaison supervision over Production Plant No. 1.

No time was lost in getting the preliminary work out of the way. By July, 1928, a contract was let to James T. Taylor of Fort Worth to cover construction of the plant buildings at Amarillo. Six months later, the Bureau's Production Plant No. 2 at Fort Worth was closed, and most of the crew was shipped to the Amarillo site. Hayes was left in charge of closing the Linde-operated Production Plant No. 1. To protect trade secrets the operating contract had given the Linde Company the right to repurchase their special separating equipment or have it reduced to scrap. With few exceptions, all items ended on the scrap pile. Cook and I moved to Amarillo; Vestal was also transferred from Fort Worth and became the Bureau of Mines' construction superintendent. Erlandson had charge of the installation of the low-temperature equipment.

The Amarillo plant (Plate IX) began operating in late April, 1929, and a week later shipped one full tank car of 98 percent helium—the best grade ever produced up to that time. The added purity over the standard of the plant at Fort Worth would have given an airship like the old *Shenandoah* an additional payload of about 10 percent. With the success of the operation established, Cook resigned just before Christmas, and six months later I was designated supervising engineer in charge of all the Bureau's helium activities outside of Washington. Erlandson was placed in charge of the plant operations.

One of the many anticipated advantages of processing gas from the Cliffside field was an assured outlet for the plant's residue gas at the local zinc smelter or the city gas main. Almost at once, however, a number of stumbling blocks arose. The first was the question of who would pay for the three miles of pipeline between the plant and the city gas main and the zinc smelter. The cost was estimated at $50,000. The government claimed the gas company should stand this expense. Company officials refused, fearing the government might go out of the helium business, leaving them with a $50,000 white elephant. On the other hand, the company was not about to permit anyone needing a gas outlet to own a pipeline connected to any of its customers. As a compromise, Mr. Cattell agreed to pay for the line, which would become the property of the gas company. The company would, in turn, reimburse the Bureau of Mines by purchasing the processed gas at one cent per thousand cubic feet above the agreed field price. In the years to follow, that extra cent paid for the pipeline many times over.

As soon as the plant started and the processed gas reached the Amarillo customers, complaints were registered from all over town. The new gas was "more difficult to light," so the gas was shunted to the zinc smelter. There, the flame it produced had an odd color that threw the operators off-stride and lowered production. A price adjustment quickly restored harmony, which has been maintained for more than three decades.

If the prompt shipment of helium from the new plant was not sufficient cause for general rejoicing throughout the Bureau of Mines, the fact that it produced helium at a cost slightly less than half the lowest cost achieved at Fort Worth surely was.

Even before the success of the new Texas plant was assured, a decision had been reached in Washington to move the Cryogenic Research Laboratory from Pittsburgh to Amarillo, where it was placed under my general supervision. The move was fortunate, for it is difficult to see how success could have crowned the efforts of the new project without the assistance of the laboratory staff under William M. Deaton, a former chemist at the Petrolia Helium Plant.

CHAPTER 6

COMPETITION
AND CUTBACKS

With the Amarillo plant off to a highly successful start, the future of the plant was almost immediately threatened by the untimely efforts of a private company to abort the Bureau of Mines' program.

Earlier, when the Lakehurst purification plant was built, the Bureau of Mines (at the request of the Navy) had placed a civilian engineer, R. R. Bottoms, on its payroll so that Bottoms could be trained to operate the plant for the Navy. Mr. Bottoms was given access to the Bureau's file of thermodynamic data and granted the opportunity to witness all experimental procedures dealing with the purification of helium. The Bureau of Mines, glad to cooperate, furnished Bottoms information concerning the engineering design of the Lakehurst plant as well as other experimental data. Two and a half years later, Mr. Bottoms was granted a patent on a helium production process—a privilege denied the members of the Cryogenic Laboratory because of a request from the Assistant Secretary of the Navy that their helium developments be treated as military secrets. Bottoms then resigned from the Navy, and obtaining financial backing from the Kentucky-Oxygen-Hydrogen Company of Louisville, Ky., built a small private helium production plant to process gas from the old Dexter gas field.

This was a difficult situation for the Bureau of Mines to cope with, just at the time it was publicly asking the Congress for funds to acquire the Cliffside gas field and to construct the Amarillo Helium Plant. Later, those backing the Bottoms process were able to obtain contracts from the Navy to supply a total of some eight million cubic feet of helium. The outside purchase of helium was another blow to the Bureau of Mines. However, in retrospect, the action of the Navy Department was justifiable in the protection of their interests. The helium-bearing gas supply at Fort Worth had reached a new low, and further decline was expected. The success of the new Amarillo plant was not fully assured. Two large airships were soon to be ordered and would be useless without helium.

Later the helium interests of the Kentucky-Oxygen-Hydrogen Company were acquired by the Helium Company, a subsidiary of the Girdler Corporation of Louisville, Ky. The Helium Company, with a plant producing helium, wanted to take over the entire production. They argued that the government price, less than half their sales price, was fictitious. They maintained that their helium-bearing gas supply at Dexter, Kan., was adequate for many years, although later they found it necessary to move the seat of their operation on two occasions because of insufficient gas supplies. Finally, the Girdler group took their case to Congress. The 1931 appropriation hearings contain over four hundred printed pages of testimony on the subject of helium, all aimed at forcing the government to secure its helium requirements from their company. The House Committee, considering the Navy Department appropriation bill of 1931, sealed the case when they reported, ". . . after a further exhaustive inquiry into the subject of helium procurement, the Committee can find no justifiable grounds for advocating the patronage of a private producer. A Government plant has been appropriated for, and built. It is in production and has demonstrated beyond dispute that it can supply Army and Navy needs for practically one-half what it would cost to buy helium from a private source." It was expected that this would end the matter. However, more was to follow. In February, 1936, when it looked like the government might furnish low-cost helium for medical use, the Helium Company initiated a plan to have the government buy them out. Consequently, when the Helium Act of September 1, 1937, was approved, it directed the Secretary of the Interior, ". . . if possible . . . to acquire by purchase all properties developed or constructed by private parties . . . for helium production . . . ." The Bureau of Mines did so, paying slightly more than half a million dollars for the Helium Company assets, which included the small plants at Dexter, Kan., and Thatcher, Colo.; and thus ended a troublesome episode.

After three successful years of helium production at Amarillo, there fell from the skies, both literally and figuratively, a terrific blow to both lighter-than-air operations and helium production. The *Akron*, the Navy's new "Queen of the Skies," and all but three of her crew of 76 were lost in a storm over the Atlantic on April 4, 1933. Among the missing was Admiral Moffett, one of the most vocal advocates of helium and the big ships. Ironically, the admiral was taking his farewell ride prior to retirement.

The *Macon*, sister ship of the ill-fated *Akron*, was not to be commissioned for some months, and the Navy had little immediate need for additional helium. In the interest of economy, both the Amarillo production and the operating crews were reduced some 50 percent. The cut affected personnel in Amarillo and Washington. One of the keenly felt losses was F. A. Vestal, assistant superintendent at Amarillo. Another old-timer to fall by the

wayside was Dr. Andrew Stewart, assistant to the chief of
the division. His wise counsel and technical writing abili-
ties were to be sorely missed.

The demand for helium gas was limited even after
the *Macon* was commissioned; and when that great ship
was lost during maneuvers over the Pacific on February
12, 1935, the helium program came very close to following it to disaster. It was difficult for many to understand
how the *Macon* could float so majestically in the air and
yet sink in the ocean. The explanation was simple. The
helium was contained in a number of lightweight cloth
cells. Each was provided with a large safety valve which
opened automatically in the event the internal pressure
rose above a preset amount; otherwise, the gas envelope
might be ruptured. When the dirigible accidentally set-
tled on the ocean, the upward thrust of the water increased the pressure on the gas bags, the valves opened
automatically, allowing the helium to escape, and the
Macon, without its lifting medium, sank helpless below
the waves. Fortunately, most of the crew were rescued.

With the *Macon* gone, the Navy had enough helium
in storage to serve its limited needs for some time, and all
helium orders for the coming fiscal year were canceled.
So, for the second time in three years, a drastic cut in the
Bureau of Mines' helium personnel was inescapable. This
time there was a better-than-even chance that the plant
would be closed permanently. I went to Washington to
see what, if anything, could be salvaged.

There was no way of escaping a major reduction in
force, and no good could come by postponing it. On the
other hand, by releasing employees as soon as reasonable
notice could be given, some $25,000 could be saved and
this money would remain available for the coming fiscal
year. Also, in the interest of avoiding a complete shutdown, the Army and Navy each agreed to transfer an
additional $10,000. An operating fund of $45,000 for

the year was thereby assured. It was agreed that every effort should be made to keep the plant in usable condition for at least another year.

While in Washington, I learned that some of the new air-conditioned buildings were in need of operating engineers. In addition, a number of good positions were located for administrative people. Thus, fortunately, most of the employees to be separated were placed in acceptable employment.

During the first six months of the new fiscal year, the plant operations were sketchy and intermittent. The crew that remained had been selected on the basis of ability to handle multiple assignments. As an example, one man could do an excellent job of welding, qualify as a machinist, and fill in as an operating engineer in the powerhouse. Trades and classifications became secondary. I took care of all of the office work, including that of janitor, and often substituted in the plant when the need arose.

Because the nature of the helium extraction process made it necessary to operate the plant 24 hours a day, the tour of duty for the employees was increased to 12 hours. After two weeks of operating continuously, everything was shut down, and the men were given compensatory leave for the overtime work.

At the end of six months, when things were getting tense, two unexpected orders for helium relieved the situation.

The Goodyear Company, which had built most of the Army and Navy lighter-than-air craft, owned a few small blimps used for advertising, and they were in need of gas. Under the Act governing the Bureau of Mines' operations, helium could not be sold but could be leased, even if there was small chance of having it returned. The lease price was made the same as the sale price. The $12,000 lease of helium to the Goodyear Company was a godsend. The fund was used to ease the overall situation in many ways.

The second unexpected order came from the National Geographic Society. The resultant lease involved a deposit of $3,000. The helium group felt that it was again in business. Even so, the plant operated only 68 days during the fiscal year of 1936.

The National Geographic Society's first stratosphere flight from the Black Hills in South Dakota had used hydrogen in the balloon. It had ended in near-disaster. To eliminate some of the hazards, the society wished to use helium for the second flight. The second stratospheric balloon, Explorer II (Plate XIII), was manned by Captain Orvil A. Anderson and Captain Albert W. Stevens. It returned to earth near White Lake, S.D., after an 8-hour 13-minute record-setting flight to 72,395 feet on November 18, 1935. The project was jointly sponsored by the National Geographic Society and the U.S. Army Air Corps.

However, about this time a catastrophe overtook the Cryogenic Laboratory at Amarillo. The organization, on which Dr. Moore had spent so much effort, passed out of existence as such and became a part of the Petroleum and Natural Gas Division, with greatly reduced funds. Much of the fundamental work underway at the time was, of necessity, abandoned. Fortunately, the American Gas Association came to the rescue with funds for several cooperative studies.

Many of the problems encountered in helium production are common to the gas industry, and at Amarillo both highly trained personnel and essential research equipment were available. Studies were made to investigate and suggest means for determining the water vapor content of natural gas, eliminating the formation of ice-like substances which often plugged gas transmission pipelines, determining the compressibility of natural gas, predicting the volume of gas which will flow through smooth pipes of various sizes and at various pressures, and determining the feasibility of removing nitrogen from natural gas to improve its heating value. Deaton, Burnett, Frost, Mullins, and others on the laboratory staff found the answers—thereby gaining international recognition for an organization that refused to die.

The giant airships were to make the headlines at least once more. Few will forget the disaster which overtook the hydrogen-filled German dirigible *Hindenburg*, which had been built in 1936. The 804-foot-long airship contained accommodations for 50 passengers. At a cruising speed of 78 miles an hour, it had a range of 8,750 miles. It carried about a thousand passengers in ten scheduled round trips between Germany and the United States before its destruction on May 6, 1937. While coming in to a delayed landing at Lakehurst, N.J., during a storm, what proved to be the last of the world's big airships caught fire in a manner never fully explained. Thirty-five of its complement of 97 perished. If the *Hindenburg* had been filled with helium instead of hydrogen, it would not have burned.

The tragic loss of the *Hindenburg* focused attention of the world on helium as perhaps nothing else could. The work of a doctor in New York City also stimulated new interest in the little-known element. Recalling the synthetic breathing mixture of helium and oxygen that Dr. Sayers and his colleagues had used for deep-sea diving, Dr. Alvin Barach tried using such a mixture for severe cases of asthma, with startling results. He reported that patients who had been brought to the hospital gasping for breath and even some expected to die, were breathing 80 percent normally within thirty seconds after being given the mixture. Showing moving pictures of actual cases, he presented proof of its effectiveness to a congressional committee considering the future of helium production.

The demonstration, coupled with Dr. Barach's assertion that he had had to watch people die who could not afford helium, contributed greatly to the passage of the Helium Act of September 1, 1937. This legislation not only made it possible for the government to sell helium commercially, but directed that helium for medical use be made available at prices which would make its general use possible.

As soon as the new Helium Act of 1937 permitted commercial sales, the Germans lost no time in applying for an export license covering nearly 18 million cubic feet for use in a new airship they contemplated putting into service. The news was enthusiastically received at Amarillo, for the requested allotment was nearly three times the plant's annual production. Plans were hurriedly put in motion to hold Civil Service examinations for the additional personnel needed, and standby equipment was put in readiness. German helium cylinders arrived in Houston, and when the Germans' agents in the United States submitted a certified check for a little over $70,000, everyone thought the order was in the bag. Not so! The request was to develop into an international hassle, with the secretaries of State and Interior, the Armed Services, the National Munitions Control Board, and even the general public getting into the act.

At one time, the Secretary of the Interior was reported to have approved a contract for the sale. After a number of delaying tactics, including a price adjustment and a reduction in the amount of the order, the reasons for the secretary's actions began to emerge. Storm clouds over Germany began to roll into war clouds. Finally, Secretary Harold L. Ickes called the whole thing off and advised the American Zeppelin Transport, "I am unwilling to assume responsibility for approving the sale for export purposes of 10 million cubic feet of helium owned by the United States."

Other foreign orders began to trickle in. Filling them was complicated with red tape. One of the most interesting orders covered the export of 220,000 cubic feet to Poland. The $4,000 contract stipulated that the Polish government, in cooperation with the National Geographic Society, planned to promote a flight into the stratosphere to be made by Captain Antoni Janusz of the Polish Air Force. The captain was a free balloonist of note and had participated in several international balloon races. The flight was to take place in Poland; but since the captain was risking his life on the success of the project, he came to this country to witness, personally, the production of the helium and the filling of the cylinders.

The captain was a charming fellow whose limited knowledge of our language lent color to his conversation. He explained his woebegone look one morning by saying he "had a revolution in his stomach."

As the first cylinders were being readied for shipment, Captain Janusz received a telegram to return to his country immediately. The cylinders left Amarillo, but whether they arrived in Poland was never known. It is known that Captain Janusz' stratosphere flight was never made. Germany had invaded Poland.

CHAPTER 7 _____

HELIUM
AND WORLD WAR II

By the time Poland surrendered in the
fall of 1939, all of Uncle Sam's large
rigid airships had been lost or decommissioned. Lacking that need for helium, production was
again at a low ebb. A few months later, however, the
Navy gave notice that it was stepping up its lighter-than-
air program. A budget request of $75,000 was submitted
by the Bureau of Mines to get the Amarillo plant in
readiness. It failed to obtain congressional sanction,
though a few days later the President approved 48 dirigibles and several lighter-than-air stations, all useless without helium.

When the Army, Navy, and Weather Bureau were
told how impossible it would be for the ten-year-old
plant to meet their projected requirements, they quickly
provided information to justify expanded operations.
They assured one and all that in less than three years the
demand for helium would certainly total 30 million cubic
feet annually. Even in its heyday, the Amarillo plant had
never produced half as much.

Fortified with this information, the Bureau of Mines
lost no time in submitting a new budget request to cover
additional production, gas pretreating equipment, and a
gas field survey. This time Congress was more cooperative, though they cut the request in half and provided it

in two sections, three months apart. The money was scarcely available when a message from the Navy brought the news that its demand alone might soon reach 50 million cubic feet a year, and the end was not in sight.

By August of 1941, the initial funds for expansion had been expended, and an enlarged Amarillo plant was operating under forced draft, producing at a rate of almost three million cubic feet of helium a month. However, it seemed certain that more helium plants would be needed on a crash basis. Congress was fully aware of the magnitude of the booming airship program and that helium was essential to make it click. Consequently, nearly 1.25 million dollars was provided for a new plant.

Within the next 14 months, successive estimates of the annual helium requirements skyrocketed to 400 million cubic feet; 200 lighter-than-air craft had been approved by the President, and nearly 17 million dollars had been appropriated for new helium production facilities.

With the handwriting on the wall, the helium operations of the Bureau of Mines, directed by "Shorty" Cattell in Washington and by me in the field, went into high gear. Don Taylor, with wide experience in the gas industry, appeared "out of the blue" and was placed in charge of engineering drafting. George Erlandson, superintendent of the Amarillo plant, directed the fabrication, erection, and testing of all the highly specialized low-temperature equipment and the training of new operating crews for the various plants. Bill Jenkins, our versatile shop foreman, assembled a crew which did a heroic job in manufacturing many items of low-temperature equipment.

Paul Mullins directed the purchasing of improved gas-treating equipment for the removal of carbon dioxide, hydrogen sulfide, and water vapor. C. C. Anderson, head of the helium gas field section, and his assistant, Howard

Hinson, directed the gas field surveys and well-drilling programs so necessary to increase the helium-bearing natural gas production. William Deaton, head of the helium laboratory, had his hands full keeping his staff ahead of demands. Earle Burnett supervised the installation of "water brakes" for the low-temperature expansion engines and performed endless engineering estimates and calculations. The administrative and purchasing activities were under the direction of W. A. Hopkins. Harold Kennedy, working with Mr. Cattell in Washington, was charged with obtaining adequate priority assistance. His success in gaining the cooperation of the various priority officials made the overall accomplishments possible.

In March of 1940, the world's only helium plant had boasted 36 employees and a production of ten million cubic feet per year. Perhaps it was fortunate we did not have a crystal ball. If anyone had been bold enough to predict that within four years we would have expended nearly 16 million dollars, built and operated four plants requiring a staff of over 400, and produced 137 million cubic feet of helium in a single year, he would have been adjudged insane. But the war was on, and work was at a fever pitch. It was necessary for the production of helium to keep pace with the skyrocketing demand.

It was obvious that a satisfactory supply of helium-bearing gas was the prerequisite of any new helium plant. The Bureau of Mines' long-maintained gas field survey paid large dividends. Its file of the nation's gas resources gave valuable information on likely plant locations. But more detailed data were necessary to establish the life of field reserves, production pressures and volumes, possible variations in gas composition, potential water supplies, shipping facilities, manpower availability, living quarters, and many kindred items which were needed for the selection of the best possible source of gas and plant locations. The small helium staff at Amarillo was not adequate for the undertaking, and highly trained help was desperately needed.

As happened so many times during the crash helium program, Mr. Cattell supplied the answer: "Borrow the necessary personnel from other Government agencies." The generous assistance of N. A. C. Smith, superintendent of the Bureau's Petroleum and Natural Gas Experimental Station at Bartlesville, Okla., and that of his successor, Harry C. Fowler, was a lifesaver. These officials supplied the services of many of their topflight engineers to study prospective helium sources and to supply other needed information. The wholehearted support and assistance given freely outside the Bureau of Mines were also most gratifying. An old friend in the U.S. Geological Survey, N. W. Bass, who had made a study of the Bureau's Cliffside field, was lent to us to make geologic studies of prospective gas fields. New friends in the Bureau of Reclamation, Spencer Baird, the Regional Solicitor, and his assistant, Fred Gray, guided our steps through the many legal mazes. The Soil Conservation Service lent valuable assistance, and officials of our own Department of the Interior gave generously of their time.

Even before money became available for the first wartime plant, it was established that the most suitable source of helium-bearing gas was a part of the Texas Panhandle gas field known as the Channing Area, some 30 miles north of Amarillo. The gas contained nearly one percent of helium, and it was being produced by the Canadian River Gas Company (now the Colorado Interstate Gas Company). The preliminary investigation made by C. C. Anderson indicated that the gas company would assign helium extraction rights and charge only seven cents per thousand cubic feet for the gas consumed, including the extracted helium. However, the rancher who owned the desired plant site had no desire to part with a single acre of his 20,000-acre cattle ranch. Finally, he agreed to sell if we would give him some of the scrap lumber sure to be left over from the plant construction. He was in dead earnest, so a deal was made which provided that we pay him $1 per load to haul off the scraps. The 320-acre plant site cost almost $5,000 and ten loads of kindling. The deal with the gas company to extract the helium from some 30 million cubic feet of gas a day was completed with comparative ease. The plant was to be called the Exell Helium Plant (Plate X), taking its name from a cattle brand.

In charge of all of the helium activities in the field and aided by Cattell and Kennedy in Washington, I prepared the general specifications. The plant was to be located 30 miles north of Amarillo, Tex., the nearest town of any size, and so it was judged essential that modern living quarters be provided adjacent to the plant. The camp of 75 houses included ones with two or three bedrooms. Garage and laundry facilities were also provided.

The negotiated architect-engineering contract for the plant was placed in the capable hands of Stearns-Roger Manufacturing Company of Denver, Colo. However, the design, fabrication, and erection of the special low-temperature helium extraction equipment was excluded from the general contract and performed by Bureau of Mines personnel.

Of necessity, Stearns-Roger looked to the Bureau for priority assistance in obtaining material and equipment. Eventually, Harold Kennedy was able to have the same priorities which were assigned to aircraft construction extended to helium plant requirements. Obtaining the necessary items was a frustrating undertaking at best. Even aircraft ratings were not sufficient to obtain some needed equipment. Often substitute items required major changes. However, by modifying compressor foundations to accommodate substituted items, rewiring large electrical generators to provide suitable voltage, fabricating pipe bends on the job, welding secondhand pipe to make building trusses and frames, and other improvisations, the project was kept on schedule.

The transportation of workmen to and from Amarillo 30 miles away was a problem. With tires and gasoline rationed, workmen required assurance of the necessary transportation before signing for work. Fortunately, our priority rating was high enough to obtain two 72-passenger semitrailer buses and tractor trucks to haul them. In the work hours, the tractor trucks hauled materials to needed points in the plant or to nearby towns on flat-bed trailers.

Just when things were beginning to level out, with orders placed for buildings, compressor and generating equipment, and other items with long delivery dates, word came from the Navy Department to increase the plant size two and a half times. They gave assurance that the needed funds would be forthcoming.

In the meantime, I had placed Carl C. ("Andy") Anderson in charge of the government's construction at the plant. He and his two assistants, George Shelton and Henry Wheeler, took the enlargement in stride. In spite of many serious obstacles, the contractor was able to complete the plant in record time and it was placed in operation March 13, 1943.

This was a time when setting and breaking records became common practice. A dedicated crew ignored the clock and overtime pay. For many of us it meant a 12- to 14-hour day, seven days a week. Helium was necessary to convoy the ships taking troops to the front, and we were determined to supply the helium on time. Little did we realize that we would have to continue this effort for nearly two and a half years.

When some eastern fabricators of copper equipment were "too busy to be bothered," I turned in desperation to a superbly equipped local machine shop.

With technical know-how and supervision from our own small force, Lowell Stapf and his Amarillo Machine Shop and Foundry crews, augmented by some 30 women substituting for experienced drill press and light machine operators, produced three-quarters of a million dollars worth of low-temperature equipment equal or superior to the best ever obtained from any source.

When difficulties arose in getting special copper pipe bends, handicapped men classified 4-F were trained to do the work in our own plant yard. Unwilling to trust the assembly of the separation equipment to unfamiliar hands, U. G. Hester, a helium plant foreman with many years of experience, collected a crew and took over that assignment with phenomenal success. Under his close supervision the Exell plant came through its test period with flying colors. Within 24 hours after startup, it was operating at 75 percent capacity or better. This same fine service was also provided for the three additional wartime plants.

Even before the Exell plant was placed in operation, it was evident that others would be needed. A new plant site at Otis, Kan., was selected. However, in order to secure the desired volume of gas, part of it was obtained from the Northern Natural Gas Company and part from the Producers Gas Company. The two streams, which were very similar, were commingled in the plant, and the processed gas was returned to the two companies on a pro-rata basis. The eagerness of all to aid the war effort was doubtless responsible for the accomplishment of this unusual agreement.

It was most fortunate that Stearns-Roger was completing the Exell plant in time to undertake a similar contract signed January 6, 1943, for the Otis plant. Paul Mullins of the laboratory staff, with plant operating experience, aided by Don Taylor as chief assistant, acted as the government resident engineer on the project.

By this time, many items of material and pieces of equipment were unobtainable. Steel could not be obtained for building construction, so trusses and columns were fabricated from lumber and bolted together—construction which has lasted for more than 20 years. Secondhand gas engines were obtained and put into service. The Otis plant put the Bureau of Mines in the pipeline business. Pipe was used to bring water two miles, and a total of more than 20 miles of gas pipeline had to be installed to get the gas supply to and from the companies' gas-treating plants.

The Otis plant (Plate X) started producing in October, 1943, just nine and a half months after the contract was awarded. During the first ten days, the plant produced 1,764,000 cubic feet of helium.

Two years after war was declared, the helium plants at Amarillo, Exell, and Otis were producing at a rate ten times that of any former period, and yet a demand for more than twice their combined capacity was predicted. At least two more plants would be required. For the moment, it seemed that finding suitable helium-bearing gas sources would be more difficult than constructing the plants. The decision was made to build one at Cunningham, Kan., but the location of the second plant remained a serious question.

A thorough investigation had shown that neither of the plants at Thatcher, Colo., or Dexter, Kan., purchased from the Girdler Corporation some five years before, could make an important contribution to the program and that the Dexter gas field was not to be depended upon.

In desperation, preliminary plans were made to use the 8-percent helium gas at Thatcher. A low field pressure and a 14-percent carbon dioxide content were definite handicaps, so the plans were made with little enthusiasm.

Then, just in the nick of time, a gas sample from the

Rattlesnake field at Shiprock, N.M., was sent to the Amarillo laboratory for analysis. We were a happy group when we found that it contained nearly 8 percent helium. The gas came from a "deep test" being drilled by the Continental Oil Company. Since the gas would not burn, the company informed Mr. Cattell they planned to plug and abandon the well known as Navajo No. 1. Before doing so, however, they wanted to offer it to the United States without cost. Eventually, the government acquired the company's interest in the well on which they had spent over $100,000 and an assignment of the lease for $1.

When the Navajo well was completed in May, 1943, it had an open flow of some 30 million cubic feet of gas per day and a wellhead pressure of 2,900 psi. It was not surprising, therefore, that it was decided to drill a second well and to build a plant near Shiprock, N.M., rather than at Thatcher, Colo.

Contracts for the last two wartime plants were let in quick succession. The first, for one at Shiprock, was let to the Hudson Engineering Company of Houston in January, 1943; and a month later the Fluor Corporation of Los Angeles signed to build a plant at Cunningham. As was the case for the plants at Exell and Otis, the government supplied many of the preliminary sketches, and designed, procured, and erected the low-temperature separating equipment.

Following the usual practice of utilizing our regular experienced laboratory and plant personnel, Bill Ferguson of the laboratory group was delegated to choose the site for the Cunningham plant. Since the Skelly Oil Company was to supply the gas for processing, a location was desired not too far from their gasoline plant near the small community of Cunningham. The site Bill picked for the plant seemed ideal. It was an elevated 20-acre plot served by a railroad and good highways; drainage of camp and plant waste posed no problem; and an ample water supply was assured. However, when the plant was half finished, we learned it was occupying a famous "cyclone ridge." Storm cellars were hurriedly added; though occasionally used by frightened occupants of the camp, they were never really needed.

For the first time the Bureau of Mines found it necessary to go outside its own organization for a plant supervising engineer. The Bureau of Reclamation lent us an excellent one, Clint B. Wood. He and his assistant, Bill Long, did an excellent job. A year after the contract was awarded, the plant was producing more than four million cubic feet of helium each month and remained a dependable source throughout the war period.

Few industrial installations as complicated as a helium plant get by without their tense moments, and the one at Cunningham was no exception. Some weeks after startup, a defective weld in a pressure vessel failed—notwithstanding the fact that it had been pressure-tested several times. Flying sections tore large holes in the roof of the separation building and, coming down, penetrated the roof of the compressor building a hundred yards away. Pieces of steel acting like projectiles cut high-pressure gas lines and filled the building with escaping natural gas. But for the courageous action of Dwight Denmead and Dale Hoyt in closing control valves before the gas could catch fire, the entire plant might have been destroyed. Fortunately, no one was injured, and the plant was back in operation in a few days.

By the time the contract for construction of the Shiprock plant was signed, the demands on the laboratory at Amarillo had fallen almost to the vanishing point, making Deaton and his chief assistant, E. M. Frost, available for assignment as the Bureau's resident engineer and assistant. W. D. Jackson, a petroleum engineer, helped them on the pipeline and gas well work.

Unlike the plant at Cunningham, the one at Shiprock was expected to become an important reserve installation. However, it was soon discovered that all that glittered was not gold.

The high helium content and wellhead pressure and the fact that nonflammable plant residue gas could be blown to the air were welcome advantages at Shiprock. Then there was the splendid cooperation of the Navajo tribal council and their desire to help the war effort in every way. However, there were a number of disadvantages. All of the plant equipment had to be trucked 90 miles from Gallup, the nearest point on a standard-gauge railroad, or 35 miles from Farmington, the closest station on the Denver and Rio Grande Western narrow gauge.

Water was obtained from the San Juan River, a mile away. Because the supply was seasonal, a complicated water collecting and treating system became necessary. A 35-mile gas pipeline was needed to bring in fuel for the plant and camp, and another 90-mile, 2-inch line was required to get the helium to the nearest tank car shipping point, Gallup, N.M. That 2-inch line turned out to be the longest high-pressure pipeline in the world. Since the helium to be transported was many times more valuable than natural gas, and was under a pressure of 2,500 psi, special precautions were taken against losing any of it. Automatic valves, installed every five miles, would close and isolate a section of the line in the event of a break or serious leak. The valves were designed by Carl Baird, one of our new recruits.

The location of the plant made it difficult to hire and keep skilled men. Fortunately, members of the Navajo tribe were dependable workers and were used wherever possible. Before the plant was completed, it became evident that most of the Navajo workers could speak English. Nevertheless, nearly all of them insisted on getting their orders through an interpreter. There were many instances similar to that of a pipeline worker who had never been heard to speak a word of English. One day he was listening at a nearby car radio to a football game. When asked if he liked football, he replied, "Yes, but I thought they'd play a much better game." He recovered hurriedly and reverted to working through an interpreter.

By March of 1944, it was clear that unless the war took an unexpected turn for the worse the Navajo plant would not be needed for steady production. So, with operators borrowed temporarily from the other plants, it was put through a successful three-week shakedown test and then placed on stand-by.

Placing the Shiprock plant and gas field in a reserve status presented a major problem. The Bureau of Mines was the owner of the lessee's rights in nearly eight thousand acres of tribal land. On the other hand, the Navajos had retained a one-eighth royalty right and were certain to insist on a reasonable amount of gas production as a means of income. The Bureau of Mines, determined to be more than fair in dealing with the Navajos, suggested a solution unique in the annals of oil and gas transactions.

Experts of the Bureau of Mines would make an estimate of the recoverable gas in the field and its value and have their estimates checked by the U.S. Geological Survey. The present-day worth would be calculated on the entire amount if produced over a 25-year period and the payment made at once in a lump sum. If more gas than that estimated was eventually recovered, the excess would be paid for separately. After verification, the figures prepared by the Bureau of Mines were approved by the tribal council, the superintendent of the Navajo service, and the Secretary of the Interior. Though not required by law, the agreement had purposely been made subject to congressional approval. Before approval, the Congress inserted a clause which authorized the Navajo tribe to sue in the Court of Claims within three years if the terms were considered unfair. Immediately thereafter, the Bureau of Mines presented to the tribe a check for $147,799 for its interests, which included one-eighth royalty on a little over 12 billion cubic feet of natural gas that would not burn. Unfortunately, the encroachment of underground water blocked the gas-bearing formation and made it necessary to abandon the field in 1958, before one-tenth of the gas paid for had been produced. Nevertheless, a few day before the three-year grace period expired, a petition was entered in the Court of Claims on behalf of the Indians, charging that the agreement was unfair. Two hearings have been held at which the government was ably represented by Floyd France of the Department of Justice. As of January, 1966, the case was still pending.

Looking back, it is clear that from Mr. Cattell on down, nothing less than an inspired group with a "service above self" attitude could have accomplished so much in such a short time. Five Army-Navy "E" awards serve as evidence in this regard. The initial presentations were made by high-ranking Army and Navy officers and accepted on behalf of the plants by officials of the Department of the Interior and the Bureau of Mines. The Amarillo and Exell plants won the award two years in succession; the Otis plant had time for only one. The Cunningham and Navajo plants were worthy candidates as the war drew to a close. In addition to the "E" awards, in which every employee participated, awards were given to special groups and even to a few individuals. Both Denmead and Hoyt received a Holmes Medal of Honor for bravery for their prompt action after the explosion at the Cunningham plant.

The guards at the plants and the gas fields were as

outstanding as the plant operating group, and in December, 1943, the Eighth Service Command presented the second Military Police Award of Merit granted in the state of Texas to the guard force of the Amarillo plant. Later, this award was also given to the guards at Exell.

The guards were under the able supervision of Colonel Rolfe of the Army's G-2 group. The colonel asked that orders be given to the guards to shoot and ask questions later if any suspicious characters were found within the plant enclosure.

One morning just before the colonel was due on an inspection trip, a boxcar was shunted into the plant and the guard who immediately checked it discovered a young boy hiding inside. When the lad was brought to my office, I decided that punishment should be left to the colonel. Upon arrival, Colonel Rolfe was reminded of his order and told that we were holding someone for him to shoot. Of course, the man from G-2 retreated rapidly, and the incident provided a welcome chuckle in an otherwise tense workday. The intruder, who had hopped the freight thinking he was bumming a ride to California, was a mighty scared young fellow for awhile. He was placed in jail while his draft card was checked. When all was found in order, he was released.

We did not learn the full implications of such drastic security measures at the helium plants until after the war's end. We knew only that helium was an essential material in our Navy's fight against the enemy's submarines (Plate VIII). In a letter dated April 10, 1944, Secretary of the Navy Knox wrote:

> The Navy Department has received a report of the shipment, on March 28, 1944, of three tank cars of helium from the Bureau of Mines Gallup Terminal, Gallup, New Mexico, to Naval activities.
>
> This shipment marks the beginning of helium production at the Bureau of Mines Navajo Helium Plant,

Shiprock, New Mexico, and the completion of expansion of helium production facilities to meet war requirements.

According to the records of the Navy Department the Bureau of Mines has increased the magnitude of its helium plants about fifteen fold and their helium production capacity at least twelve fold during the past three years. Furthermore, about two-thirds of this expansion has been accomplished during the latter half of this three year period.

This expansion has kept pace with the increase in helium requirements of the Naval service. At no time during the present emergency has it been necessary to curtail Naval uses of helium or to revise plans for use of helium because of shortages or prospective shortages of helium.

The Navy Department is fully aware of the magnitude of the work just completed, and of the competent engineering and the careful planning which has been required to keep pace with increasing requirements. The Navy Department congratulates the Bureau of Mines on this outstanding achievement.

The Bureau of Mines and its activities have at all times cooperated with the Navy Department to the fullest degree in meeting helium requirements. This cooperation is a very important factor in the smooth and successful functioning of the Naval helium supply service. The Navy Department takes this opportunity to express its appreciation of this cooperation.

Some of us knew that many thousand cubic feet of helium had been shipped to the Manhattan Engineers District of the Army, but we did not know for what purpose. Consequently, we were as shocked and amazed as the rest of the world when on August 6 and August 9, 1945, the purpose was demonstrated at Hiroshima and Nagasaki. Later, we were told by General Leslie Groves, head of the Manhattan Engineers District, that without helium there would not have been an atomic bomb.

CHAPTER 8

HELIUM
AND THE
POSTWAR YEARS

As the war drew to a close, helium was being produced at over 14 times the peacetime consumption. It was a foregone conclusion that a drastic curtailment of helium production would follow the end of hostilities. It was anticipated that many of the blimps would be decommissioned and that the demand for gas to fill them would drop sharply. No new major use of helium had been developed. So when V-J Day arrived in August of 1945, the plants at Cunningham and Otis were quickly shut down and placed on stand-by. Activity at the Amarillo plant was confined to filling and shipping cylinders with helium received from the Exell plant, the only one in operation.

The gas supply that the Skelly Oil Company had made available to the Cunningham plant was nearing depletion. Orders were given to strip the plant of usable equipment and to make the remainder available for transfer to the War Assets Administration for sale or other disposal. Needless to say, the retrenchment required a drastic reduction in force. More than two hundred excellent workmen had to be separated from the service, and our efforts to find new jobs for these men were only partially successful.

There were some, of course, who insisted that it was foolish to hold any of the helium plants on stand-by. They argued that the plants might never be needed. Fortunately, the wisdom of the more far-sighted experts in the Department of the Interior prevailed. It was not long before all of the stand-by plants were needed to keep pace with growing peacetime uses for helium. By 1951 the demand warranted the reactivation of the Amarillo and Otis plants, and in 1953 the Navajo plant was restored to active service. Helium-shielded arc welding had become a new and exciting tool in industrial fabrication.

During the war, the impossible was often attempted with surprising success. When magnesium, which is both lighter and stronger than aluminum, was suggested for aircraft, industry accepted the challenge. Magnesium is also used to make flashlight powder, and tons of it were used for incendiary bombs. As might be expected, many of the early magnesium castings were imperfect, with rejects running as high as 50 percent. New techniques had to be developed to permit its use as a structural metal.

In an attempt to salvage the defective castings, the Northrop Aircraft Company developed an electric welding torch which blanketed the molten metal of the weld with an atmosphere of inert helium. They dubbed the process "heliarc" welding. With this process, it was possible to reclaim 90 percent of the faulty magnesium castings. The process also provided industry with a new tool and a means of fabricating other hard-to-weld metals.

However, it soon became evident that the standard helium purity of the time (98.2 percent) left something to be desired. The less than 2 percent nitrogen contained in the helium was the villain. Welds produced in an atmosphere of pure helium were so superior that the wartime helium purity standard became unacceptable.

Back in the days of the Bureau of Mines' Fort Worth helium laboratory, Eastman, Finklestein, and I had shown that 100 percent pure helium could be obtained by passing a relatively impure helium through refrigerated charcoal. By adapting this laboratory technique to large-scale plant operations, George Erlandson, with help from William Deaton and Bill Ferguson, soon had helium plants producing 99.995 percent helium. No helium of less than 99.995 percent purity has been sold by the Bureau of Mines since 1950. The demands for this product, which became known as Grade A helium, have grown by leaps and bounds. The uses for helium have become diversified, and the wartime helium baby has truly become a peacetime bonanza.

The Department of the Interior arranged late in 1953 for an independent outside engineering study to determine where the helium program had been, where it was going, and how efficiently it was being run by the Bureau of Mines. The subsequent report of the Boston firm Stone and Webster was entirely complimentary. It supported the Bureau's contention that an additional helium plant was needed, and it recommended further that some attention should be given to the assurance of future, as well as current, helium requirements.

Funds were appropriated for a new plant to be located at either Keyes, Okla,. or Exell, Tex. By the time these funds became available, however, it was evident that production from a new plant could not be obtained in time to avoid a severe helium shortage. Therefore, Harold Kennedy and Henry Wheeler started in Washington an informal but highly successful allocation system to insure that the available helium reached the most important needs. It soon took the full-time service of a diplomatic expert. Under Henry Wheeler, Q. L. ("Cap") Wilcox of the Washington office did a superb job. The Helium Act provided that government agencies had first call on helium, and when shortages to defense contractors became involved, shipments to many of our old commercial customers had to be curtailed. When the situation was explained they cooperated splendidly without the use of forms or questionnaires. The cooperation of suppliers throughout government and industry was most gratifying.

Had it not been for an "ace in the hole," 100 million cubic feet of helium previously injected into the Cliffside field, the situation might have become tragic. By withdrawing some 85 percent of the stored gas over a three-year period, hardships resulting from the scarcity were greatly relieved.

The gas of the Keyes field, Cimarron County, Okla., contains 2 percent of helium. The Bureau had watched the development of this area since the first well was drilled in 1943. It was undoubtedly the best helium-bearing gas field in the country when Congress made funds available for a new plant. The Colorado Interstate Gas Company controlled most of the field, but production had been limited as the gas had a low heating value and was not readily acceptable by the company's Denver customers. However, the removal of nitrogen, if it could be accomplished economically, would improve the heating value of the gas and make it marketable. It appeared that a joint undertaking to remove both the nitrogen and the helium at the same time might be feasible, and the Bureau of Mines and Colorado Interstate Gas Company agreed to cooperate in an investigation of this possibility. The company employed the Stearns-Roger Manufacturing Company of Denver to make a feasibility study, with much of the required technical data to be supplied by the Bureau of Mines. The report of this study provided so much encouragement that in June, 1955, final negotiations were underway for helium processing rights to the Keyes gas. Then the Bureau of Mines learned of an insurmountable legal difficulty, and the project was temporarily abandoned.

Two months later, with helium in short supply, a contract was let to Stearns-Roger covering architect-engineering work to enlarge the Exell plant, where Colorado Interstate Gas Company could supply additional helium-bearing natural gas for processing. E. M. Frost, chief of our division of engineering, supervised this expansion.

The new project was carried on without adversely affecting the production of the already existing facilities—an achievement for which the general contractor, Quaker Valley Construction Company of Tulsa, deserves great credit. It was completed in June, 1957, adding 150 million cubic feet of helium a year to the helium production capacity.

It was expected that the Exell expansion would make the allocation of helium a thing of the past. However, the demand had grown at such a rate that it was necessary to continue allocation. The need for another plant was inescapable.

The Bureau of Mines had never given up the idea of obtaining the rights to process gas from the Keyes field in Oklahoma, and with good reason. Over 600,000 wells had been drilled in the United States since the Keyes field was discovered in 1943, and no comparable helium source had been found. In early 1958 it was gratifying to learn that conditions which had forestalled earlier negotiations no longer existed. In April of that year a contract was signed with the Colorado Interstate Gas Company for an exclusive right to extract helium from the Keyes gas.

No time was lost in completing a contract for the construction of a new plant at Keyes, an undertaking supervised by R. D. Haynes. Don Taylor had charge of plant layout and acted as resident engineer. The Fluor Corporation of Los Angeles started work in November, 1958, and nine months later the plant was in production.

113

The Keyes plant (Plate X) is similar in many respects to the older Bureau of Mines plants, but it also employs many modern improvements. Expansion turbines running at 65,000 revolutions per minute are used in the refrigeration cycle instead of the old-fashioned reciprocating expansion engines, and strategically located instrumentation and controls make the operation of the plant almost automatic.

The Bureau of Mines helium installations are unique in that they have been self-sustaining. Helium has always been sold at a price which paid for operation and maintenance of the plants. In addition, commercial charges have included sums to cover amortization and interest and a small capital reserve.

The extraction process of all the plants is similar and includes several steps. A simplified description follows: If necessary, gas from the field is compressed to at least 450 psi. It is then treated to remove water vapor and carbon dioxide. (The 0.3 percent of carbon dioxide in the Keyes gas removed daily amounts to 10 tons.) If not extracted, they would freeze and plug the system. Next, the incoming gas must be cooled to a temperature of −300° F. This is accomplished by using the nitrogen which has been removed from the gas and compressed to 600 psi to run a small engine or turbine. The energy used by the nitrogen in performing this work is lost in the form of heat, so the nitrogen leaving the engine is appreciably cooler than when it started. The exhaust gas is made to cool that entering the prime mover, and the cycle is repeated until the necessary low temperature, about −320° F, is finally obtained. That temperature causes the compressed gas to liquefy, except for the helium and some nitrogen. On leaving the plant, the liquid is made to cool the incoming gas and is itself warmed and returned to a vapor state. The processed gas, now at room temperature, goes back to the gas company for distribution to its customers. The gaseous mixture of helium and nitrogen, a 60-40 crude, is compressed to 2,700 psi and progressively cooled to the temperature of liquid nitrogen boiling under reduced pressure. As a final step, the helium, now about 99.5 percent pure, is passed through coconut charcoal refrigerated to the temperature of liquid nitrogen. The product is grade A helium, 99.995 percent pure.

The government's newest plant, at Keyes, Okla., has demonstrated its ability to produce one million cubic feet of grade A helium a day, 40 times the capacity of the first plant at Amarillo. Helium is no longer allocated, and its uses are growing.

There remained the problem of shipping the helium. Next to hydrogen, helium is the lightest of all elements. One thousand cubic feet of helium would just fill a spherical balloon 12½ feet in diameter and would weigh 10½ pounds. For shipment, the helium is generally compressed into steel cylinders. The usual small cylinders weigh 130 pounds but hold only two pounds of helium. It took the gas from 13,000 such cylinders to fill the *Shenandoah*. When empty, they must be returned for refilling. Often the cost of shipping to the East or West Coast and returning the empty container amounts to three times the f.o.b. plant charge for the helium.

As a means of reducing both transportation and handling costs, the Army developed special railroad tank cars (Plate VI). Each of the early ones consisted of three heavy-walled steel cylinders 40 feet long, mounted on railroad trucks. At a pressure of 1,800 psi, 180,000 cubic feet of helium could be compressed into them. The cars weighed 100 tons empty; the helium filling them weighed less than a ton. Modern cars are heavier, having 28 or 30 cylinders of smaller diameter. They are charged at higher pressures and are able to hold more helium. The replacement value of the government's fleet of 233 tank cars is over 20 million dollars. They are just as necessary as the plants.

Smaller versions of the tank cars have been developed for highway travel. In addition, nearly a quarter of a million cylinders holding about 200 cubic feet each are shipped each year. This is not quite the end of the transportation story. Unusual and exacting precautions are necessary to prevent the 99.995 percent helium from becoming contaminated. All cylinders are evacuated before filling. Oil-lubricated pure helium compressors are avoided like the plague, and the outgoing product is continuously checked for purity prior to entering the shipping container.

In an effort to further reduce freight costs, consideration is being given to the large-scale shipment of helium in liquid form. One cubic foot of liquid will evaporate and produce 754 cubic feet of the gas at ordinary temperature and pressure. With the solution of some special problems, liquid helium may eventually offer the cheapest form of transportation.

CHAPTER 9

HELIUM
AND THE FUTURE

Those in the know have been discussing helium conservation for years. As far back as 1920 the National Advisory Committee for Aeronautics wrote the Secretary of the Interior that due regard should be given to conserving sources of helium for military purposes. Six months later, the Bureau of Mines' Dr. Moore wrote the Army suggesting that the entire Texas Panhandle gas field of that time with its desirable helium content might be purchased for one million dollars. More than half a million dollars worth of natural gas a day is now being sold from that field and its extensions.

As early as May, 1921, the helium potential of the Cliffside field was recognized, and J. O. Lewis of the Bureau of Mines recommended its acquisition. In 1922, the subject was discussed by President Harding and his Cabinet, and on March 3, 1925, the first Helium Conservation Act was passed.

In less than two years, arrangements were made to purchase the Cliffside field and its two billion cubic feet of contained helium (perhaps twice as much in the light of present knowledge). Based on predicted demands, it was expected to supply the country's helium needs for a hundred years. Two small helium-bearing gas sources on public lands in Utah were also set aside as helium reserves.

By 1957 the picture had completely changed. The Rattlesnake field acquired from the Navajo tribe, and upon which so many hopes had been pinned, was no longer a dependable source. It was equally certain that the ballooning helium demands would deplete the Cliffside field in short order. (At the 1960 rate, it would be depleted in ten years.) All of this time more than five billion cubic feet of helium a year was being transported to the fuel markets with the natural gas and lost forever to the atmosphere when the natural gas was burned. As the reserves were depleted, the available helium would become less with each passing year, and by 1985 the gas being produced would fall short of supplying the country's helium needs. What could be done?

During a briefing session with O. Hatfield Chilson shortly after he became Under Secretary of the Department of the Interior, I stressed the terrific waste of helium going to market each day with fuel gas and expressed my fears that a critical shortage was certain to develop within twenty years. Mr. Chilson became intensely interested and arranged a two-hour conference to discuss the situation in detail. This conference, which set the stage for the many conferences and actions to follow, was perhaps the most important two hours in the history of the government's multimillion-dollar helium conservation program.

The Under Secretary was able to interest some of the country's top officials in helium conservation. At the suggestion of Gordon Gray, director of the Office of Defense Mobilization, four work groups were established, with the Under Secretary of the Interior as chairman. The membership was drawn from high-ranking officials of the departments of Commerce, Interior, and Defense, the Atomic Energy Commission, the Bureau of the Budget, the Office of Defense Mobilization, and the Bureau of Mines. The opinions of leading scientific advisors to the

President, Dr. J. R. Killian, Jr., and Dr. A. P. Waterman of the National Science Foundation, were sought. The consensus: helium conservation was a "must" and it should be implemented without delay.

Fortified with the reactions of such an array of talent, Secretary of the Interior Fred A. Seaton decided the situation should be brought to the attention of the President and his Cabinet. They, too, approved the program. In August, 1958, the secretary sent Congress a draft of needed helium conservation legislation. Authority for an effective helium conservation program was subsequently provided by the Helium Act Amendments of 1960, enacted September 13, 1960.

The new legislation provided an opportunity for government and industry to work together in partnership in the new program. Industry was invited to participate in building and operating plants to extract the helium from fuel gas. After the helium had been extracted, the gas would continue its journey to fuel customers. The government would purchase the helium, under contract, from the private plants and store it in the Cliffside field (Fig. 2) for the future. The government would then sell helium to consumers at a price which would make the project pay for itself in a 25-year period. The program had the full support of President Eisenhower. Its initial objective was to save approximately 52 billion cubic feet of helium, in addition to meeting current demands over the 25-year period.

The Act resulted in the building of five plants and contracts for the purchase of nearly 50 million dollars worth of helium each year for the next 22 years, to insure available helium to serve the needs of our children and grandchildren.

Underground storage in the Cliffside field is in the Bush Dome—a well-defined structural feature lying 3,500 feet below the surface and occupying about 11,000 acres

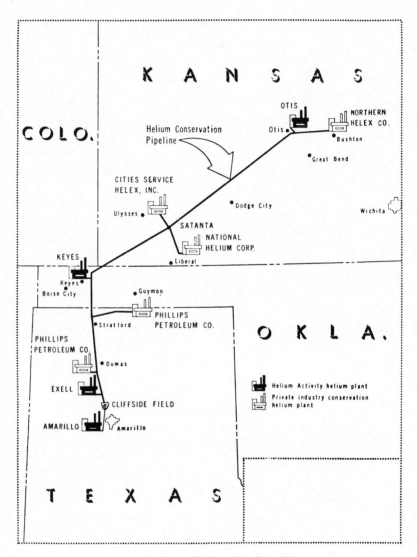

FIG. 2. Bureau of Mines Pipeline System

of the 50,000 acres comprising the field. The dome-shaped, porous, and permeable rock stratum is 120 to 200 feet thick, and the apparently solid rock has a myriad of minute interconnected openings. These openings contain helium-bearing natural gas which will be displaced gradually by stored crude helium. Helium is injected in the center of the field, and native gas containing helium is withdrawn from the outer edge of the field. Helium has been successfully injected and withdrawn from the field on an intermittent basis since 1945.

CHAPTER 10

PERSONAL REFLECTIONS

Since my retirement in September, 1959, the responsibility for the free world's supply of helium has been shifted to other shoulders, and I have had time to visualize in retrospect my 50 years' association with the wonder gas.

There was a time, many years ago, when I looked upon the idea of commercial production of helium as the figment of a wild imagination. And I remembered that earlier time as I watched TV one day in February, 1962, and listened to the countdown that was to send John Glenn into orbit. My thoughts turned backward to a few small flasks of "useless" helium in Dr. Cady's laboratory, to Sir Richard Threlfall's "ridiculous" suggestion of using it to fill dirigibles, to associates who had labored in laboratories, over drafting tables, and in machine shops, to plant operators and office workers, each of whom would share in the success or failure of that history-making event. I knew that helium was helping to force fuel and oxygen to the big engines of the Atlas (Plate XIII) and was keeping the outer skin taut. I realized that Glenn's voice would come back from outer space amplified by means of a small ruby crystal in a bath of liquid helium. As the countdown reached zero I thought with a glow of pride of the many people who had worked so long and against such odds to make helium available for such a fantastic feat; and I, too, said, "A-OK."

I remembered, too, that when I had checked the purity of the first shipment of some 700 cylinders as it started to the World War I front, my whole concept of the project had been in terms of thermodynamics, heat exchangers, compressors, and expansion engines. I know now that such things are not responsible for the development of today's large-scale program from yesterday's chemical curiosity. Rather, it has been built by the Cadys, the Moores, the Cattells, and their like—men with vision who would not accept defeat; men who were not afraid to take chances on uncharted paths, whose zeal, enthusiasm, and integrity rubbed off on those who knew them and worked with them. If I, too, have been such a boss, if I have helped those who have risen through the ranks to places of authority and leadership, I am content.

In taking a final backward glance at these many-sided helium undertakings, I feel that our successes were due to more than men of vision, more than careful planning and supervision, more than willing and competent workers. The solution to a hopeless situation too often appeared out of the blue, too many unforeseen incidents caused pieces of complicated puzzles to fall into place, the entire program was saved from failure too many times for me not to recognize the presence of an unseen hand helping at crucial moments to guide us onto the wise course. For this Providence I am humbly grateful.

However exciting and productive the early years of helium have been for me, they are now history. I hope it is a history that will go on repeating itself, that new problems will continue to receive the utmost from dedicated workers who will grow in knowledge and in ways to apply it. Then, surely, the years ahead will hold many additional opportunities for utilizing helium, the "child of the sun," in the service of man.

The wise and efficient use of the nation's helium resources took on an important new dimension late in 1962 with the launching of a national helium conservation program authorized by the Congress. In December the first of five contractor plants began delivering helium to a 425-mile Bureau of Mines pipeline system, which carries the gas into an underground storage reservoir, Cliffside field, near Amarillo. All five plants were in operation by July, 1963, and by the end of that year about 300 million cubic feet of helium a month was flowing into storage. Formerly, this helium was wasted to the atmosphere when the natural gas containing it was used as fuel.

The five plants were financed, designed, and built by four companies to deliver a crude helium mixture under 22-year government purchase contracts. Over the life of the contracts, an estimated 62.5 billion cubic feet of helium will be conserved. The average composition of the crude helium mixture delivered by the contractors is about 71 percent helium, 27 percent nitrogen, 1 percent hydrogen, and 1 percent methane. But the government pays only for the helium.

Northern Helex Company's Bushton, Kan., plant (Plate X) was completed in December, 1962. It was designed to process 500 million cubic feet of helium-bearing natural gas a day with a helium content of about 0.46 percent to produce an average of 675 million cubic feet of helium a year. The plant (Plate XI) completed by Phillips Petroleum Company in Hansford County, Tex., in December, 1962, was designed to process 200 million cubic feet of gas a day containing about 0.71 percent helium. Another Phillips plant (Plate XI), completed in April, 1963, at Dumas, Tex., can process 275 million cubic feet a day of 0.66 percent helium content gas. The average annual production of the two Phillips plants totals 790 million cubic feet a year. Completed in June, 1963, Cities Service Helex Inc.'s Ulysses, Kan., plant (Plate XI) can produce 500 million cubic feet of natural gas a day containing 0.43 percent helium for an average annual helium volume of 610 million cubic feet. National Helium Corporation's Liberal, Kan., plant (Plate XI), completed in July, 1963, was designed to process 840 million cubic feet of gas a day containing 0.40 percent helium to produce 1,050 million cubic feet of helium a year.

Helium demand during the period covered by the contracts will exceed the capacity of the government's own plants, all five of which are operated by the Bureau of Mines. Consequently, some of the purchased helium will not go to storage but will be purified and sold. Just how much, of course, depends on how much helium is used and on how much of the demand can be met by a small but growing private helium industry which is distinct from the firms that are participating in the helium conservation program.

This private sector has been developing since 1961 despite the phenomenal growth of helium sales from Bureau of Mines plants, which increased from 475 million cubic feet in 1960 to 809 million cubic feet in 1966. The development grew out of the realization that industrial uses for helium had created a substantial and reliable market, big enough to justify the risk of private capital on production and distribution facilities even though the federal government remains the major helium user and must, under law, obtain its supply from its own plants.

The first of the modern private helium plants, built by Kerr-McGee Corporation, near Navajo, Ariz., has an annual capacity of about 65 million cubic feet. It began operation in December, 1961. Helium-bearing gas for the plant is obtained from company developed sources in the

Pinta Dome field. It contains 8.2 percent helium; the remainder is essentially nitrogen. In December, 1963, a 12-million-cubic-feet-a-year plant was built near Swift Current, Saskatchewan, Canada, by Canadian Helium Limited. During 1966 the company announced plans to triple its capacity. In April of 1966 a plant having an announced capacity of 180 million cubic feet a year, built by Kansas Refined Helium Company near Otis, Kan., began operation. The output of this plant is liquid helium, which is purchased by the Air Reduction Company and transported in 10,000-gallon semitrailers to distribution points. There most of the helium is vaporized and compressed into standard containers as gas; some, however, remains as a liquid and is ultimately used in that form. Late in 1966 a 140-million-cubic-feet-a-year plant built by Alamo Chemical Company and Gardner Cryogenics near Elkhart, Kan., neared operational status. Plans call for production and marketing of gaseous and liquid helium.

Contrary to expectations, sales from Bureau plants did not drop when the privately owned plants began operation. This can be attributed primarily to the fact that the growth in helium demand has been faster and far more substantial than anyone had anticipated. No doubt the availability of helium from non-government sources helped to spur increased use of the element in such fields as metallurgy, undersea work, chromatography, and cryogenics. As long as the government was the sole source of supply, industry did not feel itself assured of continued access to helium. Many industrial users remember the periods of helium shortage between 1950 and 1959 during which an informal allocation system was used intermittently to channel available supplies to defense-related projects. Hence, the emergence of other sources has doubtless helped to encourage industrial utilization of helium in a variety of applications where it offers unique advantages.

Completion of the Gemini program and preparation for Apollo accounted for much of the growth in helium demand during 1966, when consumption totaled about 960 million cubic feet. Of course, even though actual demand has closely approximated the Bureau's projections thus far, no one can say with certainty what future helium requirements will be or exactly how helium will be needed in years to come. It does seem certain, however, that helium will continue to be an important element in the technology of tomorrow. The value of helium stems from its combination of unique properties. That is the reason for its conservation—to insure full, wise, and effective use of those properties. Unless the helium now being removed from fuel gas and saved for the future is to be used, its conservation is without purpose.

The question of whether helium conservation is justified has been considered seriously in recent years by several groups representing government, industry, and the scientific and engineering community. Each group has arrived at essentially the same conclusion: Helium is worth saving now to assure its being available in the future. But, despite the number and intensity of these studies, one major question remains unanswered: "How much helium should be saved for future use?" Although the present program is stemming the waste of this irreplaceable resource, more than three billion cubic feet of helium continues to be lost each year as fuel gases containing it are burned.

The Helium Act requires that all costs of the program be liquidated within 25 years. Right now, during the early years, income from helium sales is not covering such costs, and the difference is obtained by borrowing from the U.S. Treasury in amounts approved annually by the Congress. As time passes, annual helium sales are expected to increase; and according to present estimates, repayment of borrowed funds should begin about 1970. A selling price of $35 a thousand cubic feet, established for helium soon after the Helium Act was passed, is calculated to pay out costs of the program as required.

The large-scale use of helium which grew with projects Mercury and Gemini should increase still more with planned Saturn launches and the manned lunar landing. Helium's combination of inertness, light weight, compatibility with other materials, and low temperature of liquefaction makes it an ideal material in space technology. In fact this element, which will help men reach the moon and return, actually preceded them there in June, 1966, when Surveyor I—carrying a tank of helium to pressurize fuel to its rocket engines (Plate XIV)—made a soft lunar landing. Upon radio command from earth the helium remaining in the pressure vessel aboard the spacecraft was released. Thus in a small way the moon had a thin atmosphere of terrestrial helium produced by the Bureau of Mines' helium activity program. The Saturn V lunar launch vehicle as it was being developed in 1966 depended heavily on helium.

The element is used in welding components for rocket structure, for checking out rocket components, and in new and larger space simulators (Plate XV) to test full-size spaceships under conditions approximating those that will be encountered in the void beyond our planet. By the time a vehicle is ready for launch, much more helium will have been used getting it ready for flight than will be required during lift-off and completion of the mission. Yet, getting Saturn V off the ground and the Apollo lunar payload to the moon and back will find helium doing many things. To begin with, one day before launch, helium will be used to check for leaks in the complex system of pneumatic controls which actuate valves and sensing elements before, during, and after launch. Helium then continues to function in the firing of the first, second, and third rocket stages. For example, the 7.5 million pound thrust propulsion arrangement for the first stage is fueled by kerosene and liquid oxygen, and warm helium is used to pressurize the kerosene so it will drain into the suction of the rocket engine pumps. A blanket of helium is placed above the surface of the liquid oxygen to protect gaseous oxygen, which is used for pressurization., from coming in contact with the liquid and condensing. If it should condense, the pressure in the tank would fall and jeopardize operation of the engines. In the second and third stages, which are fueled with liquid hydrogen and liquid oxygen, helium is used to purge the vent lines and engines of explosive hydrogen until the engines are ready to fire. Later, it pushes liquid hydrogen into pumps which supply the engines. Liquid hydrogen is so cold that it will freeze any gas but helium. That is why helium is used for purging hydrogen tanks and lines and for pressurizing the liquid.

Even during holding time on the launch pad, helium plays an essential role. It keeps air from penetrating the thin insulation on the liquid hydrogen tanks and accumulating on the tank as many unwanted pounds of liquefied or frozen air. This is accomplished by a stream of helium flowing between the tank wall and the insulation. Also, during holding time, a stream of helium bubbles into the liquid oxygen just above the inlet to the pumps to prevent warming of the liquid oxygen, all three million pounds of it. Otherwise, the oxygen might reach a temperature that would keep the engine pumps from working. Or, it might even build enough pressure to rupture the fuel tank or destroy piping. A small amount of oxygen evaporates in the helium bubble, thus cooling the liquid the way water can be cooled in a porous jar on a hot dry day. After ignition, when engine thrust is built to lift-off proportions, helium actuates the hold-down clamps which release the bird for its flight from earth. Helium will also be on board the Lunar Module which, with the Command and Service Modules, will be hurled into low earth parking orbit before starting the trip to the moon and back. When parking orbit is reached, the third-stage J-2 engine shuts down, and the vehicle coasts for about four hours. Then, once more with an assist from helium, the engine starts and injects the Apollo payload into the lunar transfer trajectory. During the coast period, helium pressurizes hypergolic propellants, which ignite on mixing to provide thrust for attitude control. The same system provides attitude control for the Apollo Spacecraft Lunar Module during turnaround maneuver of the Apollo Command and Service Modules. When this is done, the third stage is jettisoned and the Apollo payload continues to the moon. Once in a parking orbit around the moon, as the astronauts enter the Lunar Module (Plate XVI) for descent to the surface, they will call on helium to pressurize fuel for the propulsion system that gets them there. In addition, by a process known as aeration, helium is injected into the propellant so the rocket engine can be throttled and the astronauts can hover above the moon surface to find a suitable landing location and make a safe descent. When they are ready to leave, the descent stage is left behind and the helium-pressurized propulsion system of the ascent stage lifts them to rendezvous with the orbiting Apollo Spacecraft for subsequent return to earth. In all of these intricate and critical operations, helium saves literally thousands of pounds of weight over other possible systems. Thus, as the plans stood in 1966, helium, in many applications, is helping to speed man on his conquest of outer space.

Helium performs other roles in the exploration of inner or hydrospace. Experiments such as Jacques-Yves Cousteau's "Conshelf," Edward Link's "Man in the Sea," and the U.S. Navy "Sealab" projects have shown that, provided with a breathing mixture of helium and oxygen, man can live and work under the sea for days, even weeks, at a time. In September, 1965, during the Sealab II (Plate XII) experiment, three teams of ten men each stayed down 15 days. Astronaut Scott Carpenter, who was among the first men down, spent 30 consecutive days at a depth of 205 feet with the help of helium. The element will also be indispensable during future Sealab experiments. Plans for Sealab III call for divers to live and work at a depth of 430 feet, with occasional dives to 600 feet. Their breathing mixture will be mostly helium with about 2 percent oxygen. Such a mixture eliminates the carefree, drowsy feeling called "rapture of the deep" which affects divers and may cause them to make a fatal mistake after breathing nitrogen-oxygen mixtures for prolonged periods. Several firms have developed equipment which utilizes helium-oxygen breathing mixtures and permits divers to work safely for days at a time on the sea floor and in lakes behind dams. With such gear, underwater crews can salvage sunken ships and repair oil wells, pipelines, and underwater structures in a fraction of the time formerly required.

In a totally different but equally important realm, helium in liquid form cools superconducting magnets. These are made from materials that lose all electrical resistance at the temperature of liquid helium ($-452°$ F). Once started, a current will flow indefinitely in such a magnet without connection to a current source so long as the magnet remains immersed in liquid helium. The combination of suitable superconducting materials and liquid helium is making possible the development of extremely small magnets that can produce intense magnetic fields. One of several such materials, a niobium-tin compound, already is used for this purpose. These magnets have the advantage of low power requirements, in addition to small size, when compared with conventional magnets. For example, conventional electromagnets require not only tons of steel and auxiliary equipment but also million-watt power supplies and the equivalent of a small river of water for cooling. Most of the energy fed to them is lost as heat. Superconducting magnets having the same output can be held in one hand and can be energized by current from a small battery.

Taking this concept a step further, a superconducting generator capable of 8000 watts of alternating current power has been developed for the U.S. Army Engineer Research and Development Laboratory, Fort Belvoir, Va. Still in the future, but becoming increasingly feasible, is direct generation of electric power by passing an ionized gas through the field generated by a large superconducting magnet. Such a system is known by the term magnetohydrodynamics, and if it becomes successful it could give operating efficiencies of 50 to 80 percent. This compares with a top performance of 40 percent in conventional steam power plants. Application of the new method would probably involve the burning of ordinary fuels such as coal, oil, or natural gas to supply the ionized gas. Helium would, of course, play a vital role by providing the low temperature required for magnet operation.

The gleaming promise of some of these prospective uses may not materialize. But others, now unknown, will doubtless be discovered. In any case, helium—child of the sun, and long produced there by the nuclear burning of hydrogen—will continue to serve man for many years.

HENRY P. WHEELER, JR.
Assistant Director—Helium
Bureau of Mines

INDEX

134

INDEX

Design: Fritz Reiber
Text typeface: Electra
Display typeface: News Gothic Condensed
Paper: Glatfelter RRR 60# Standard White
Endleaf: Canfield Paper Co. Canco Duplex Endleaf
Printer: University of Kansas Printing Service
Binder: State Printer